Habitats and Territories

BASIC TOPICS IN
COMPARATIVE PSYCHOLOGY

Julian V. Jaynes, EDITOR

HABITATS AND TERRITORIES

A Study of the Use of Space
by Animals

Peter H. Klopfer

Basic Books, Inc.

PUBLISHERS

NEW YORK : LONDON

598.25
K 695

EDITOR'S PREFACE

STUDY of the evolution of animal behavior is having a remarkable development in our time. Research in this field is moving forward over an immense spectrum of species and behaviors and on a wider front than anyone would have dreamed possible only a quarter of a century ago. And the range of method is enormous: from meticulously manipulated situations in the laboratory to careful ecological observations on expeditions all over the world; from punctate electrical stimulation and recording of single brain cells in different phyla to mathematical theories of animal population and ecological distributions. Out of this new accumulation of facts and observations is coming a variety of new theories of animal behavior, of evolution itself, and of the nature of man that are and will continue influencing present civilization in important ways.

In any such rising tide of science, a most important problem is keeping good communication on the advancing fronts. *Basic Topics in Comparative Psychology* is a series of nontechnical books of the highest scientific standard designed to meet this need. Each book is an introduction to an important area by a recognized leader in that area and is intended for the scientist in a related area, for the university student in zoology or psychology, and for the layman who wishes to keep abreast of recent advances in the study of animal behavior. With comparative psychology going through its period of fastest development, it is hoped these books will make progress more solid and sure by gathering disparate discoveries.

JULIAN JAYNES

PREFACE

LET ME, first, say what this work is not: it is not a comprehensive review of the character and kinds of animal territoriality; it is not a comprehensive review of the literature on habitat selection; nor is it a textbook of animal ecology. However, elements of these areas may be found in the pages that follow.

What I have sought to do is introduce the more fundamental concepts concerning the distribution of animals in space to students for whom biology, and, specifically, ecology and animal behavior, are alien fields. Why are animals not randomly distributed in space? What are the physical, biological, and social factors that influence distributions? How do these act? My intent has been to illustrate the manner in which biologists are seeking the answers to these queries. It will be evident that students of psychology and the social sciences, whom I hope particularly to reach, could shed much light on the search.

PETER H. KLOPFER

Durham, N. C.
March 1969

ACKNOWLEDGMENTS

A PARTICULAR DEBT of gratitude is owed Jeremy J. Hatch and Jack P. Hailman, whose intellectual companionship means much to me. Others who read and offered criticisms of this book are Drs. David Singer and Robert Sommer. I do thank them, as well as my inestimable secretary and factotum, Mrs. Catherine Dewey. Financial support for my own work described herein has come from the National Institutes of Health and an NIH Career Development Award. Finally, because I have never previously done so—and it is fitting that it should come about—I dedicate these pages to Erika, Lisa, and Gretchen.

CONTENTS

Habitats and Territories

1

HETEROGENEITY OF THE HABITAT

"In the course of its advance from a germ to a mass of relatively great bulk, every plant and animal also advances from simplicity to complexity. . . . At the same time that the parts into which each whole is resolved become more unlike one another, they also become more sharply marked off. . . ."

H. Spencer, *First Principles* (1896)

The Significance of Heterogeneity

ALMOST ANY PHYSIOGRAPHIC ATLAS provides illustrations of the patchwork pattern of our planet: here there is a yellow patch of low desert, there a Rorschach blot of montane forest, and over there broad streaks of upland prairie. Even as the scale is increased, the patches remain evident. On a large map the North Carolina Piedmont may appear uniform, but a drive along a Piedmont road dispels the illusion: a north-facing slope is capped with cool, dense beech trees; on the facing slope, toward the bottom, is a stand of tulip-poplar trees; above these oaks and hickories. But a few yards farther on, on an exposed flat, stand torches of loblolly or a cultivated field. We could increase the scale still further; for even at the level of single particles of sand, patchiness in the physical substrate remains compellingly evident.

In the aquatic environment graininess is also an important feature. Solutions, of course, are uniform dispersions, but natural bodies of water are never merely solutions. Gradients—often extremely sharp—of temperature, salinity, and organic debris combine to stratify, partition, and subdivide all but the smallest, wind-mixed puddles. Nor is the atmosphere homogeneous. Both stable and labile differences in moisture content, oxygen pressure, air movement, and temperature, among other things, differentiate air masses that lie over different parts of the earth or at different altitudes. An Alpine chough (a crow-like bird of high altitudes) flying at an altitude of 20,000 feet is not in the same environment as a suburban robin; nor is a sea bass in the same environment as a freshwater carp. But although it is obvious, even trivial, to observe that the earth's surface and adjoining regions—the life-inhabited region named the *biosphere* (Vernadsky, 1945)—is heterogeneous, the consequences of this heterogeneity are considerable and not altogether obvious.

For illustrative purposes, let us construct a uniform environment: a fish bowl containing filtered, aerated water that is continually mixed, has a controlled temperature, and has a constant, but limited, supply of nutrients. Now let us add several individuals, each of several species of protozoans. We can observe the growth of the protozoan populations over several days by periodically taking a count of small samples drawn from the fish bowl. One set of results, illustrated in Figure 1–1, shows that in a homogeneous environment, a population made up of individuals all of which belong to the same species grows, first, exponentially, then asymptotically. When the individuals belong to two species, the population of only one grows, that of the other declines. It is not always possible to predict which species will decline and disappear, but, in any event, in a homogeneous environment two species cannot coexist. When heterogeneity is introduced, however, as by adding bits of straw to the bottom of the bowl, then both species may thrive. Thus, under

uniform conditions with at least one resource in limited supply—
for instance, food or space—only one species of animal can exist
continuously.

The reasons for this competitive exclusion were not made explicit until long after the generality itself had been established (by
Grinnell, 1904). However, reflection will suggest an explanation:
no two species are identical in appearance or behavior. Thus, no
two species will be equally efficient in extracting energy from any
given uniform and stable environment and in reproducing them-

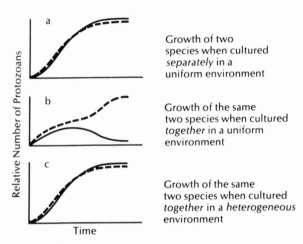

FIGURE 1–1. Growth of Protozoan Populations in Uniform and Heter-
ogenous Environments. (Based on Gause, 1942.)

selves. Therefore, the more efficient species must eventually sup-
plant the others. The fact that a wood is inhabited by many different kinds of birds, a continent by even more, is directly attributable
(in part) to the heterogeneity of the environment and the character
of interspecific competition.

This last point can be illustrated in yet another way. Imagine a
savings bank which pays two of its depositors slightly different interest rates—4 per cent and 4.1 per cent, for example. This slight
difference in the rate of interest represents a difference in extractive
or reproductive efficiency (a difference in selection). Further, assume that the bank has only a limited capacity (finite resources);

as soon as the combined value of its two depositors' accounts equals $1,000, each depositor must withdraw a part of his holdings, so as to reduce the sum of their holdings to $500. However, each depositor's share of this $500 is proportional to his original share of the $1,000. If the depositor's holdings grow only as a consequence of the accumulation of interest (natural increase), it is possible to specify the date by which virtually all of the money will belong to the party with the slightly higher interest rate. This outcome must eventually occur, however small the difference in interest. (For a detailed exposition of differential reproduction and its effects see R. A. Fisher, 1958. Or, for a less difficult account than Fisher's, see MacArthur and Connell, 1966).

The Principle of Competitive Exclusion

The hypothesis that no two species will have identical extractive and reproductive efficiencies in any specified (uniform and stable) environment is a logical derivative of Darwin's theory of evolution by natural selection. Indeed, the Darwinian concept of competition specifically refers to competition in this sense, rather than to the direct struggle—animal against animal—implied by the literalists' "nature red in tooth and claw." The power of the hypothesis, known today as Gause's Rule, or the "competitive exclusion principle" (Hardin, 1960), lies in its heuristic value: it is directly susceptible to experimentation in two ways. First, we could proceed from an examination of a natural situation and from it infer the explanation for the continued coexistence of related species, and second, we could simulate a simplified and controlled environment. One of the most elegant examples of the first approach is a study of a group of warblers which live together, each in much the same way as the others, within the northeastern coniferous forests (MacArthur, 1959). But, as shown in Figure 1–2, the various species have actually subdivided the forest trees: individuals of one species feed predominately near the treetops, whereas those of another prefer to be close to the trunk; a third has chosen the outermost portion of the branches, and so on. Without the environmental heterogeneity provided by individual trees and exploited by

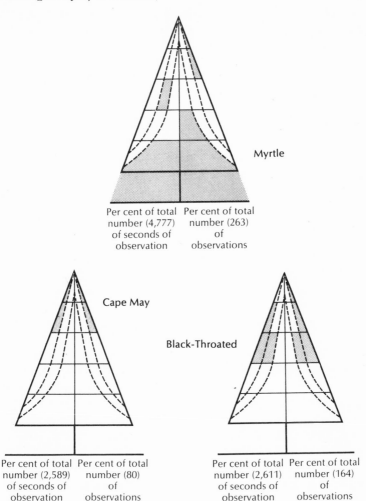

FIGURE 1–2. Activity Graphs of Three Species of Warblers. Myrtle, Cape May, and black-throated green warblers coinhabit the same New England spruce woods. These three diagrams represent the portion of time these birds spend in different zones within the trees. The tinted areas show where the majority of activity is centered: Note the differences, which have the effect of reducing competition for food between these species. (Based on MacArthur, 1958.)

the birds, behavioral diversification of the warblers would have to be reduced and, as a result, fewer species could coexist. It is not necessary that the birds always position themselves in this way, but during that period of the year when the growth of the populations is subject to environmental limitations such as nest sites, available food, or shelters, it is essential.

Diversification of habits does not depend solely upon fine spatial divisions, such as those illustrated by the warblers, but can also depend on heterogeneity in the food supply. For example, if bill sizes of two otherwise similar birds differ, these birds may tend to feed upon different size classes of insects or seeds. It has been claimed that any difference in bill size that will produce significantly differentiated food preferences must be about 3 per cent, i.e., the ratio of the length of the larger to the smaller bill must be at least 1.3. The same minimum ratio probably exists among beetles jointly occupying a particular habitat (Hutchinson, 1959).

It often happens that two species co-occur in some parts of their individual ranges but not in others. For instance, two species of Darwin's finches of the Galapagos Archipelago have bill lengths of 10.5 mm. and 10.8 mm., respectively, on the two islands where they are found separately. On a third island, where they are found together, their bill lengths are quite different. The bill length of *Camarhynchus psittacula*, which measures 10.5 mm. on Bindloe Island, *shrinks* to 8.5 mm. on South Albemarle, whereas the bill length of *Camarhynchus pallidus,* which is 10.8 mm. on Chatham Island, *grows* to 11.2 mm. on South Albemarle.

A similar relationship has been noted among several species of rodents, as well as other birds and insects. Because the divergence in size appears only where two species are in contact (generally termed "character displacement," Brown and Wilson, 1956), morphological differentiation probably reduces competition. The validity of the underlying assumption that differences in bill shape or size reflect differences in feeding habits has been examined empirically. Consider the four steps that can be recognized when a bird feeds: (1) the psychological choice of food, (2) the acquisition of the food, (3) the preparation of the food for swallowing, and (4) ingestion and digestion. One recent study has focused upon (1) and (3), food choice and food preparation (Hespenheide, 1966). To obviate the difficulties presented by factors of taste, nutritional value, etc., which have confounded many other studies, the two test species, the North American white-throated sparrow and the slate-colored junco, were tested with only one seed—the sunflower—the size of which could be varied. The junco's and white-throat's bills differ only slightly in length. Whether the difference actually exceeds the ratio of 1 to 3 depends on the axis measured. However, despite the slight difference in bill structure, the junco took 64 per cent of its seeds from those in the smallest size class and 14 per cent from the two largest, while the white-throat took 45 per cent from the smallest size class and 17 per cent from the two largest. Measures of the white-throat's extractive efficiency in dealing with seeds of different size were also made. The data obtained, although inconclusive, did suggest that the preferred size of seeds accords with the size most efficiently handled. Thus, the relative choice of different sizes of the same seed is different for two bird species of slightly different bill size, and choice of seed types is probably correlated with a bird's speed in opening these types.

Preferences may also exist in the absence of overt morphological constraints. For example, newly hatched, inexperienced garter snakes apparently prefer worm scents to cricket scents, but a related green snake has the opposite preference. And since both snakes are found in the same area, these differences may well reduce food competition. However, whether the cause of these preferences can be pinpointed in the peripheral or central nervous system is not known (Burghardt, 1967). Among the hooved mammals, many species of which graze together, it is assumed that there are distinctive foraging preferences, with some mammals selecting one herb, and others different ones. In this regard, the vast and heterogeneous herds of the plains of Serengeti provide marvelous research opportunities which have yet to be fully exploited. Of course, it is possible that some other, as yet unspecified, mechanism controls the severity of interspecific competition. Ungulates, unlike birds, might utilize the same foods and in the same proportions. The bloody wars between the sheep and cattlemen in the American West attest to this fact: sheep forage on the same grasses as do cattle. However, because they crop more closely than cattle, sheep preclude the coexistence of the bovines.

Another factor which can cause food competition among animals to be reduced is activity cycles of the several species that differ. If one species feeds nocturnally and the other by day, food competition may be avoided. Thus, disregarding other differences, barn owls and barred owls are compatible, since the former often feed by day and the latter almost never do. Thus, the barn owl can both tap resources not available to its nocturnal neighbor and share commonly used resources as well.

The main point to be drawn from studies of food use and competition is that situations in which species with similar requirements coexist are rare. Any exceptions are apparently caused by temporary conditions—i.e., a period of superabundance of food or a shift in the direction of competition. If environmental conditions are constantly changing, the same species may not always be favored; and, if the fluctuations in conditions are sufficiently rapid, there may be insufficient time for either species to become extinct. First one, then the other, will dominate, and no static equilibrium can be established. In such a case, the heterogeneity is temporal, rather than spatial, but this does not reduce the significance of environmental heterogeneity, for without it, species diversity could not be maintained, indeed, would not have arisen.

An alternate approach to naturalistic studies of competition—which seeks to simulate a limited and controlled environment to allow for a specification of equilibrium conditions and to identify the mechanisms of competition—is one that is more restricted and analytic in scope than the one we have been considering up to now. The best known examples of this second approach are studies of flour beetles (see Park, 1962). When representatives of two species of these beetles are placed in a uniform mass of flour, only one species invariably survives, although if the beetles are introduced in equal numbers it is not always possible to predict to which species the survivors will belong. But, when reproductive rates differ slightly, or when differences in egg cannibalism exist, predictions as to which species will survive can be made. Changes in the environment, the addition of bits of macaroni, or allowing the lower levels of the flour to become more densely packed will alter the competitive relationships in a specific fashion. For our purposes, however, we should bear in mind the support these studies lend to the view that environmental heterogeneity is the *sine qua non* for the coexistence of two or more similar species.

In summary, there is considerable biological significance to patchiness of environment on earth. We shall enquire further into the causes of this patchiness, although not in detail. But the answer to the question of why the earth's surface is heterogeneous must largely be provided by geologists, geochemists, and meteorologists. The answer will also be part historical, dependent on the manner of the earth's origin. And it will be in part dependent on the asymmetric orientation of the earth with regard to the sun and the consequent inequalities in the distribution of solar energy. We must also consider the other asymmetries that have produced the localized glacial and pluvial intervals, the effects of which on the surrounding substrate can be observed for centuries after (note Flint, 1957).

Patterns of Heterogeneity

So far we have attempted to convey some notion of the significance of the heterogeneity of the earth's surface. Now we will examine and describe the bases of some of the classifications into which habitats have been ordered. If it were possible to classify all habitats according to some small set of criteria, classification would pose no problem. For instance, if temperature or moisture or even some combination of temperature and moisture was the essential factor limiting the distribution of different species, habitats could be ranked along some appropriate scale of temperature and humidity. Unfortunately, there is little basis for believing that a simple table of "limiting factors" can be described for any organism, and hence, there is even less reason to expect that we can classify habitats on such a basis. This requires some amplification, since many introductory ecology texts dwell at some length on the concept of limiting factors or Liebig's "Law of the Minimum" (e.g., Odum, 1959), and have re-enforced the belief that the Law affords a basis for habitat classification. This Law states that "the essential material available in amounts most closely approaching the critical minimum needed will tend to be the limiting one" (Odum, 1959, p.

88). With rare exceptions, however, the value of the so-called "critical minimum" will vary with other factors. For example, a tree that cannot tolerate nocturnal freezing temperatures when the air is dry or the soil is packed or the days are hot may survive if the air is moist, or the soil is loose, or the daily range of temperature is reduced. The interactions between a variety of factors led to the formulation of a less restrictive "Law of Tolerance" which is sometimes substituted (Shelford, 1913). The ability of an organism to maintain itself in a given habitat is thus seen to be dependent on a complex of conditions that are within the organism's range of tolerance. However, this looser formulation has proven to be unsatisfactory because it is circular and of no heuristic value. In short, organisms generally prove to be too diverse and too complex with regard to the conditions they can tolerate to allow for a classification of habitats on the basis of some manageable number of parameters. One solution to this dilemma, if it can be called a solution, has been to base habitat classifications upon a Gestalt character intuitively perceived by naturalists. Another has been to select a feature of the environment that is believed to be basic to the overall structure of the habitats. We will first consider an example of the latter class.

Climatic conditions generally vary systematically from the South Pole to the North Pole, a direct consequence of the earth's rotation and tilt with regard to the sun. The pattern of land and sea masses produces modifications of the gross planetary patterns of circulation and heat exchange, and, on a finer scale, so does the pattern of mountain ranges. The vegetation that prospers in a particular area, in turn, may reciprocally influence climatic conditions by altering the rate of return of water to the atmosphere, interfering with air flow or altering the extent of solar re-radiation. But, if we ignore local effects such as the latter, it is possible to prepare a climatic atlas of the earth and to devise a classification of the earth's regions. One of the more popular (and useful) of these schemata is Glenn T. Trewartha's modification of Köppen's system (Goode, 1950) (see Figure 1–3). This particular schema differentiates among five major regions on the basis of temperatures and rainfall, which, in turn, influence soil characteristics, vegetation, and, thus, all habitats. The major regions are further differentiated into a

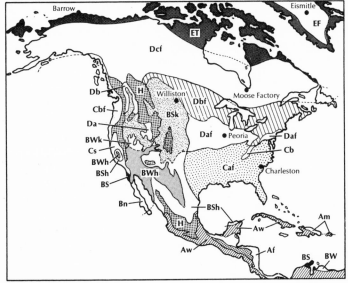

TYPE REGIONS AND SUBTYPES

A — Tropical forest climates: coolest month above 64.4°F. (18°C.).

B — Dry climates (for limits see graph at right. p. 9).
 BS — Steppe or semiarid climate.
 BW — Desert or arid climate.

*C — Mesothermal forest climates: coldest month above 32°F. (0°C.), but below 64.4°F. (18°C.); warmest month above 50°F. (10°C.).

*D — Microthermal, snow-forest climates: coldest month below 32°F. (0°C.); warmest month above 50°F. (10°C.).

E — Polar climates: warmest month below 50°F. (10°C.).
 ET — Tundra climate: warmest month below 50°F. (10°C.) but above 32°F. (0°C.).
 EF — Perpetual frost: all months below 32°F. (0°C.).

a — Warmest month above 71.6°F. (22°C.).
b — Warmest month below 71.6°F. (22°C.).
c — Less than four months over 50°F. (10°C.).
d — Same as "c," but coldest month below −36.4°F. (−38°C.).
f — Constantly moist; rainfall all through the year.
*h — Hot and dry; all months above 32°F. (0°C.).
*k — Cold and dry; at least one month below 32°F. (0°C.).
m — Monsoon rain; short dry season, but total rainfall sufficient to support rainforest.
n — Frequent fog.
s — Dry season in summer.
w — Dry season in winter.

Modification of Köppen definition

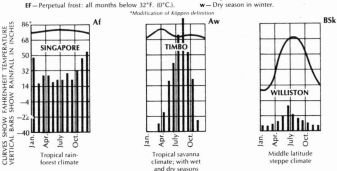

FIGURE 1–3. An Example of Köppen's Climatic Atlas (as Modified by Trewartha). The letters code climatic conditions, as indicated. (Based on Goode, 1950.)

dozen subtypes which are defined in terms of climatic extremes and stability.

Another classificatory system was devised by C. H. Merriam (see Kendeigh, 1961) for North America. The "life zones" of Merriam, for the most part, followed isobars of temperature and ignored other variables. The choice of particular isobars of temperature as the limits to the various zones was based upon the distribution of certain plants and animals, these species being particularly abundant or conspicuous. Thus, the "life zone" classificatory system, while seeming to depend upon a physical parameter—temperature—is actually an organism-based system. The use of distributional data for classification constitutes the second "solution" referred to above.

Before we can apply a classificatory scheme to the earth's habitats and their inhabitants we must define operationally our units of measurement and the entities to which they will be applied—a difficult and frustrating problem. To begin with, the basic "functional unit" of the environment has been termed the *ecosystem* (Tansley, 1935): "any area of nature that includes living organisms and non-living substances interacting to produce an exchange of materials between the living and non-living parts" (Odum, 1959, p. 10). Ecosystems may vary in size from an aquarium to an ocean, but their "functional" character is not precisely definable, nor can the boundaries between adjacent ecosystems be unambiguously demarcated. Ecological systems have themselves been divided into *biomes,* units which are "easily recognized" (Odum, 1959, p. 386) by a uniform vegetation or animal assemblage. Typical biomes are the temperate deciduous forest, coniferous forest, tropical forest, plains, tundra, and desert. That these biomes are often easily and intuitively recognizable would be foolish to dispute. That they can be defined by firm operational criteria has yet to be demonstrated despite many efforts that have been made to demarcate and identify discrete pieces of the distributional checkerboard. These efforts have spawned a variety of terms: *formations, associations, associes, biociations,* and *biocies,* among others (see Kendeigh, 1961). They have also led to a controversy as to whether one can meaningfully distinguish groups of species from one another, however large or small, in a manner analogous to the distinctions between climatic regions made by Köppen. On the one hand have been the ecologists who felt that certain groups of species, or communities, form supraorganisms; and on the other have been those ecologists for whom each species must be treated separately. The former notion lends itself to a recognition of groups of even larger compass, and could provide a basis for defining biomes. The latter, more individualistic view, is difficult to reconcile with any broad classificatory scheme.

Evidence for the view of the community as a supraorganism rests, first, upon the correlation between the distributions of certain species and second, upon the interdependence these species show in their energy exchanges. For example, a typical pasture community (described by Odum, 1959) might include bluegrass, clover, some oaks, cattle, a variety of birds, and numerous soil organisms. Their interrelationships become evident when any one of them is removed: slaughter the cattle and trees will likely replace the grass, which, in turn, will alter the avifauna. Poison the soil organisms and the texture of the soil will change, leading to the destruction of the grass and clover and starvation of the cattle. In short, a web of relationships connects the disparate elements of this community, causing even small perturbations to be felt widely. In natural situations—i.e., undisturbed by man—communities differ widely in their susceptibility to disturbance, but, to a greater or lesser degree, they exhibit the homeostatic control characteristic of conventional organisms. For instance, when the dominant predator has only a few prey organisms available to him, as would be true of the carnivores of the far north (lynx, wolf, and fox), the number of his prey is likely to oscillate wildly, with a concomitant effect upon other faunal and floral elements of the community. When many alternate species of prey are available, i.e., when the web of relationships is larger and more complex, disturbances are effectively damped. Thus, the view of the community as a supraorganism must also entail the notion of degrees of organismic complexity and homeostasis.

The opposing view, which rejects the notion of supraorganisms, is based largely on a detailed analysis of species composition and distribution within so-called communities. For instance, the distribution, i.e., density, of some of the more common species found within fresh water and terrestrial habitats has been plotted against various environmental gradients such as altitude (Whittaker, 1956). Plots of the densities of the different plant species of an area against altitude should, if the concept of the community as a supraorganism is correct, produce a family of curves with their peaks clustered together. The result, however, can be seen in Figure 1–4: a cluster of heterogeneous curves which appear to be independent of one another. The implication is that, regardless of the energetic relations between different species, differences in their

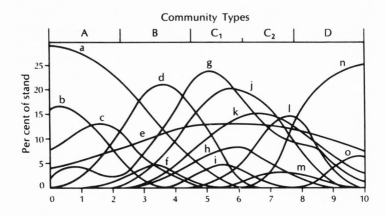

FIGURE 1–4. The Evidence against the Community-Concept. Each of these curves represents the distribution of one species of tree as a function of distance up a mountainside. Ecologic conditions change gradually as one moves up the mountain, but the species of trees that compose the plant "community" do not change concordantly. (Based on Whittaker, 1956.)

tolerances to environmental variables will assure a high degree of independence in distribution. The apparent distinctiveness of natural communities must then be attributed to our human penchant for surveying but a small aspect of the total scene, seizing upon one or two especially conspicuous or common (so-called "indicator") species, or upon a similarity in growth forms that may be imposed upon many different species by a particular environmental regimen, e.g., acid conditions, shallow or saturated soils, etc.

Despite the evident discordancies in the distribution of peak densities, as found by Whittaker, the probability of finding oaks in a beech wood is significantly greater than the probability of finding pines in a beech wood; similarly, a competent birdwatcher can predict, from a knowledge of the trees he observes, the birds he is most likely to encounter (although, as we will learn later, this prediction can be made on the basis of tree form as accurately as on the basis of tree species identification). The co-occurrence of groups of species, either with a greater or lesser exchange of energy between them, does not require either that the distributions of the species be 100 per cent correlated, or that rigid boundaries exist between these groups; nor does it preclude the existence of overlapping groups whose species may be thought to share membership in several "communities." In short, although distributions of individual species can be shown, at a fine-grained level of analysis, to vary relatively independently of one another, at a coarser level of analysis we can recognize species clusters even though we may not always clearly demarcate them from one another. For convenience, we label these clusters "communities"; whether there is any functional value to describing them as supraorganisms has yet to be demonstrated.

We can summarize the above as follows: organisms are not randomly distributed over the earth's surface; rather, they are clumped together. Depending upon the observer's scale, i.e., the degree of "graininess" that he wishes to detect in the picture, clumps of certain species are more often than not found together. Such clusters of associated species are variously termed communities, associations, or biomes; they occasionally share in an obligatory energetic or reproductive relation, but it is doubtful whether the clusters can be operationally demarcated in terms of some such functional characteristic (for an opposing view, note Odum, 1959). And, further, since the distribution of the component species of the biomes or associations or communities may be affected in varying degrees by the different environmental parameters—temperature being, perhaps, of primary importance to one species, soil conditions to another—the maximum densities of the component species may not be achieved at the same locus. Here, too, the "grain" or scale effect will be relevant. For our present purposes, the most significant observation derives from the fact that the character of plant and animal distributions is such that given a partial faunal and floral description of a field or woods, it is possible to complete the description without a firsthand examination: loblolly pines and spruces are not found at the same location, but if loblollies are present, sweetgum trees can also be expected.

2

ON SPECIES
AND THEIR NUMBER

The Species Concept

BEFORE WE TURN to a consideration of the determinants of the diversity or differences in diversity found in various areas, let us first clarify our notion of species (see Mayr, 1963). Individual animals can be recognized, defined, and, generally, delimited from their environment, with the exception of microorganisms such as certain viruses, which we will here ignore. However, individual plants or animals have no *distributions,* show no differences in density or diversity: density and diversity are characteristics of populations of individuals. And populations of similar forms are often referred to as *species.* It is of more than semantic importance that we give this last notion greater precision. There are countless examples of the importance of so doing; for example, there recently appeared in *Nature* a report on the fine structure of the salt-excreting nasal gland of "*the duck,*" no further identification being provided. The usefulness of the author's detailed description was vitiated by the fact that the functional prowess of avian salt glands varies both according to the species and the habitat in which the bird is reared. Thus, Pekin ducks reared on 2 per cent saline show considerably more development of the salt gland than is shown by Pekins reared on fresh water (Schmidt-Nielsen and Kim, 1964). Mallards, from which domestic Pekins are derived, are usually fresh water dabblers. Presumably, the normally marine eider ducks would prove to have the most highly developed of anatid nasal glands. Therefore, a description of the nasal or salt gland of "the duck" is, in effect, a portrait of an anonymous person. In short, we must develop a clear notion of the concept of a species.

The use of binomial nomenclature—the designation of each creature by generic and specific names—was initiated by Linnaeus in the eighteenth century. From that time through the mid-nineteenth century, classification was typological, that is, species were composed of morphologically similar individuals that, to an arbitrarily determined degree, resembled an idealized "type individual." With the Darwinian revolution, the notion of species was gradually transmuted until it came to refer to an assemblage of organisms of such close genetic relationship as to permit interbreeding. The species was then defined as a group of individuals capable of breeding among themselves and not with members of other groups (see Huxley, 1943). Since the degree of genetic relationship is generally mirrored by the degree of physical similarity—except for sexual differences—the change in the species concept produced relatively few practical nomenclatural problems. However, it did raise other questions: How does one classify self-fertilizing plants? These may never exchange chromosomal material with other individuals. Is each individual to be considered a separate species? Or, in the case of very similar appearing organisms inhabiting opposite sides of a continent, how could one know whether they were capable of interbreeding? Or, consider the extinct forms of the paleontologists: Two individuals living at different times certainly could not interbreed, however similar in appearance or closely related. Must "fathers" and "granddaughters" be considered separate species? While these objections may seem trivial they do force us to admit that we need more than a single species concept: That of the paleontologist must necessarily be typological; that of the botanist must make allowances for the commonness of self-fertilization—to say nothing of polyploidy, hybridization, etc. (see Stebbins, 1950). Even within the province of zoology, at least four categories of species must be recognized, as will be noted below.

The basic concept of the species remains in all cases that of a group of cross-fertilizing forms capable of producing fertile offspring among themselves but barred from successful genetic intercourse with others. The barriers to successful hybridization may be (1) gross physical differences, as when the pollen of members of one species does not fit into the slot of the stigma of another, (2) chromosomal, as when a variety of cytochemical differences prevent chromosomal pairing, or (3) behavioral, as when mating preferences or activity periods of courtship routines differ greatly. But this basic concept is also affected by the biological realities which ignore limitations on our ability to specify the degree of interbreeding possible to any particular populations.

The first kind of species comes closest to the ideal: this includes the *stable, sympatric species* (i.e., occupying the same habitat within the same geographic area), separate intrafertile groups that reside together. The blue- and golden-winged warblers of the eastern United States are an example. Occasionally, blue-wings and golden-wings do hybridize, producing two morphological classes of young that were previously believed to represent distinct species (Brewster's and Lawrence's warblers), but the proportion of these hybrids is not increasing. Thus, despite some slight commingling, the blue-wings and golden-wings do maintain their genetic distinctiveness and their specific identity, and they do occupy the same woods.

This situation may be contrasted with a pair of *labile, sympatric species* (second category), such as Fowler's toad and the American toad. The American toad's breeding season begins earlier in the spring than does the Fowler's, but some late Americans may be reproductively active at the same time as early Fowlers. The two then hybridize readily in some geographic regions of overlap, producing fertile young whose own breeding period is intermediate to that of the parental generations. Thus, the degree of overlap in successive breeding periods increases, as does the probability of hybridization. As this situation continues, the separate identity of Fowler's and American toads will likely disappear and the two species will merge into one. At the present time, one must be resigned to their being "separate species, but not quite!"

The third category of species comprises *stable, allopatric species* (i.e., geographically separated), such as the populations of polar and Kodiak bears. Despite superficial differences in appearance, these bears have proven in zoo experience that they are capable of interbreeding and producing viable, fertile young. (It could be argued, of course, that these young would not prove viable in the wild. For present purposes, however, we can legitimately assume that they are fully viable in all circumstances.) The possible degree of interfertility of these two types of bears is largely irrelevant, however, since their wide natural geographic separation bars them from intercourse as effectively as any chromosomal barrier.

Finally, we must recognize the complex category of *Rassenkreise*, or chains of populations with varying degrees of geographic contiguity and differential fertility. Populations *A* and *B,* for instance, which are contiguous, may produce infertile young on crossbreeding, and thus each population is accorded specific status. However, both *A* and *B* individuals may be fully interfertile with individuals from population *C*, which is more distant geographically from either *A* and *B* than *A* and *B* are from one another. Or, individuals of *A* may be interfertile with individuals from the contiguous population *B*, and *B* individuals with those from contiguous population *C*, although the geographically separated populations *A* and *C* are not interfertile. Such complexities are particularly common among circumpolar animals, such as certain gulls (see Figure 2–1).

Speciation and Adaptation

Spatial isolation is thought by most biologists to have been the prime factor in the accumulation of small, random mutations such as lead to the divisions of populations. What is a single breeding unit can, upon geographic separation, become two. This does not preclude other means for the generation of species. *Polyploidy*, the doubling or trebling of chromosomes in a single, saltatory step, is not uncommon among plants, and, if the polyploids cannot cross with the parental stock, a new species can be said to exist. Speciation by saltation is not thought to be common, however, though Goldschmidt (1955) disagrees and exemplifies the lack of unanimity about this view among even the most eminent geneticists. In addition, it is believed that abrupt changes in habitat preferences (i.e., changes occurring in one generation) can lead to the division

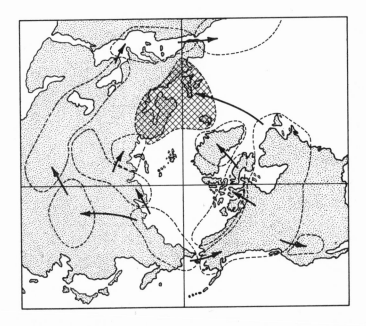

FIGURE 2–1. Example of a Rassenkreis. The geographic ranges of various races of herring gull are shown on this polar view of the globe. These races are not reproductively isolated from one another (i.e., they can interbreed freely) except in the crosshatched region. Two races coexist there, the terminal races of the chain, and they are not capable of reproduction *inter se*. (Based on Mayr, 1963.)

of one species into two without geographic separation (*sympatric speciation*). If, for instance, the habitat preferences of an individual are a function of early experience, then a fortuitous circumstance or a single aberrant individual may initiate a new species. Consider insects which habitually oviposit upon a particular plant. Certain races of the cabbage moth, *Pieris rapae*, for instance, select radishes, others, cabbage or turnips. If the eggs of the radish-loving race are transferred to cabbage—as may occur by accident or through the behavior of an abnormal female—the insects hatching from these eggs will presumably prefer their natal plant, choosing to remain in its vicinity and mating preferentially with others of like disposition. They will thus segregate themselves from their radish-loving forebears. Admittedly, this form of speciation is speculative, and no other more convincing examples are known at the present time.

Once a population is divided with regard to reproduction and gene flow, the two halves can be expected to become morphologically different. This is due both to the accumulation of minor, random changes and to natural selection favoring different genotypes in different situations, i.e., to differential adaptation (for further discussion about adaptation, see p. 92). It should be emphasized that speciation and adaptation are not the same phenomenon, and adaptation to different environments does not necessarily lead to speciation. The independence of the processes of speciation and adaptation is most pronounced when the adaptation is a change in response-flexibility. We can emphasize this point by distinguishing "adaptation" from "adaptability" (see Gause, 1942). The distinction is best made by considering the response of an organism to a new environment. If the organism survives the new conditions, we say that it has made an adaptive response. This response is due in part to an initial innate or genotypic adaptation and in part to subsequent, phenotypic (i.e., affecting the corpus rather than the genes) modifications (although, of course, these, too, are ultimately gene-determined). The initial states of individual susceptibilities are referred to as adaptations, and the capacity to make a subsequent response, adaptability. Thus, the heavily pigmented skin of some human beings, which is present from birth, might represent an adaptation to ultra-violet rays, whereas the capacity to form pigment (or to tan) upon exposure to ultra-violet rays would be considered to be an instance of adaptability.

In a series of experiments dealing with the tolerance of protozoans toward saline solutions, there is found to be an inverse relationship between the capacities for adaptation and adaptability (Gause, 1946). Let the capacities for adaptation be represented by *a*, and adaptability by *b*; *a* + *b* = *k*, a constant. If *Paramecium caudatum* is gradually acclimatized to ever-increasing salt concentrations, the clones derived from the acclimatized populations will prove to be highly tolerant to larger concentrations of salt (high value for *a*). Their capacity to tolerate sudden changes in salt concentration, however, will be reduced (low *b*), as compared with clones derived from nonacclimatized populations. In short, it appears that a genetic response (adaptation) limits the magnitude of physiologically analogous phenotypic responses. Environments in which conditions vital to the welfare of particular organisms fluctuate will not favor the development of adaptations; rather, there will be a premium on the development of adaptability. Changes toward greater flexibility might be expected to be less likely to lead to speciation than the changes we have called adaptations. We shall return to this point when we consider the causes of species diversity.

On the Numbers of Different Species

We began Chapter 2 by indicating that one of the characteristics of a heterogeneous environment was that it permitted the coexistee of different species. Moreover, species differentiation is facilitated by the heterogeneity of the environment: a number of different species is apparently able to exploit a heterogeneous environment more efficiently than is a single species. If we make a crude measure of environmental heterogeneity, however, we find that similar environments do not always have the same number of species. What, then, determines the species diversity of an area? In the discussion that follows, we shall first provide an operational definition of species diversity, then describe a method for specifying the degree of environmental heterogeneity, and finally, provide a statement that quantitatively relates the former to the latter.

The simplest measure of the number of species occupying an area is a direct count or faunal list. Such a measurement is apt to overlook rare species, of course, but repeated sampling can minimize this danger. A more serious problem is that a simple count does not allow one to discriminate between casual visitors, accidentally introduced through flight, or between migrants and breeding residents. The accidental visitors' impermanence makes their presence ecologically meaningless; they surely should not be counted on a par with the residents. To surmount this difficulty, the census may be restricted to breeding individuals. Except for birds, which are easily counted during the breeding season, this type of census may pose practical problems because many animals are *least* conspicuous when breeding. A further complication is that such a census will vary considerably with the area sampled: breeding birds are territorial, but the territories of different species (or even of individuals of the species) vary greatly in size (see Chapter 3). There is a mathematical "solution" which allows one to make a reasonable prediction of the effect on one's census of an increase in the area censused (Preston, 1948). But there is yet another difficulty. Assume that a particular wood has 100 individuals, of which 25 belong to each of four species. A second wood, of similar size, also containing 100 individuals, has 97 of one species and one of each of the remaining three species. It would seem that the latter wood had "fewer species." However, all that we can rationally state is that one wood has a much higher diversity of species than the other, even though the actual number of species represented is the same. In this instance "diversity" has become a measure of the probability of one's being able to predict the species to which the next individual encountered belongs. If 97 members of the population belong to one species, the prediction can be made accurately, on the average, 97 times out of 100. If only 25 per cent belong to one species, the accuracy of prediction will fall to one in four. A useful index of diversity would be related to the difficulty of guessing a species correctly: the more diverse the fauna, the more difficult the guess would be. The index devised by MacArthur (see MacArthur, 1965) is a variant of the measure of uncertainty in information theory. Suppose there are two equally common species; one may guess A to be the correct identification; whether this is right or wrong, no further guesses need be made, since if A is wrong, species B must be correct. Suppose, now, that there are four equally common species (A, B, C, and D). The most parsimonious form of guessing is first to guess "either A or B"; if this is correct, one would then guess A, but if this is wrong, then one would guess

C. Either way the species would be identified in two guesses. The problem of eight equally likely species requires three yes-or-no guesses, and so on; the number of guesses (G) is the logarithm (base 2) of the number of species (n): $G = \log_2 n$. The probability (p) of occurrence of each species is $p = 1/n$, so that $n = 1/p$. Substituting $1/p$ for n yields: $G = \log_2 1/p$, which may be rewritten $G = -\log_2 p$.

If the species one is trying to guess is not equal in abundance to the other species, the number of yes-no guesses must be weighted by the relative abundance of the species in the population, that is, its probability of occurrence (p). Thus, $G = p(-\log_2 p)$, and the *average* number of guesses needed to identify *any* individual to species is the sum of such terms: $Gavg = -\Sigma p(\log_2 p)$. Furthermore, it does not matter to which base the logarithm is taken (so long as one system is used throughout), so that MacArthur has defined bird species diversity (BSD) in terms of the natural logarithms:

$$\text{BSD} = (-\Sigma p_{ln})(p).$$

To cite an example (MacArthur, 1965), a population with 99 individuals of one species, and one of another, would lead to this calculation:

$$(-\Sigma)(-P_i)(\log_e)(P_i)(-P_2) = (-0.99)(\log 0.99)$$
$$-(0.01)(\log_e 0.01) = .0560.$$

A population of 50 individuals of each of two species would yield $(-0.5)(\log 0.5) - (0.5) = 0.693$. MacArthur goes on to point out that where all of N species are equally common, each represents $1/n$ of the total, so $-\frac{1}{i}E_1^n P_i \log_e P_i = N(1/N \log_e 1/N)$, which equals $\log N$. This allows us to convert each of our two diversity indices to a measure of "equally common species" (E). The number of equally common species is the logarithm of that number, E, of equally common species, which has the same diversity as N, unequally common species. In the first population, above, $e^{0.0560} = 1.057$, and for the second, $e^{0.693} = 2.000$. 1.057 and 2.000 thus become the final measure of species diversity, measures which accord well with the intuitive perception. The information-theoretic index is not necessarily the best measure of diversity for all cases; however, it is extraordinarily useful for those cases in which the census-taker can provide nose-counts as well as a species list. In the discussion that follows, "diversity" will, in fact, refer to this particular measure.

Describing the Environment

Our next problem is to specify operationally *environmental complexity*. Again, we may be intuitively aware of the greater heterogeneity of a tropical rain forest, as compared with a bamboo forest, but reliance on intuition does not lend itself to generalizations of a more quantitative, powerful nature. We can, of course, attempt to list habitat "morphologies" and then describe an area in terms of the number of "morphs" it contains. The following is an example of one such scheme which is appropriate for birds (Emlen, 1956). Three major features of the habitat can be recognized: (1) vegetation, including height of the top and bottom of the canopy, the screening efficiency of the canopy, the foliage and twig type, and the coverage and degree of plant dispersion, (2) substrate, including ground slope, ground water, and soil type, and (3) special features, such as bodies of water, barren areas, and human artefacts. Specific units of measurements for the items that compose each major feature are then employed in such a way that a particular habitat can be described by a particular "formula" or group of formulae. Ignoring the specific measures used, you may note that an African acacia thorn veld becomes $(B2^{8M-}_{20E})$ $(G2^{1M}_{100})$, and an oak opening in the northern United States $(B3^{15M}_{101})$ $(B3^{15D}_{1501})$ $(G2^{4D}_{90M})$. Such hieroglyphics (even if one remembers the meaning of the symbols) are of dubious advantage over straightforward descriptions, since they may provide wholly misleading impressions of similarity or difference between two habitats. These units of measure are both arbitrary and nonequivalent; they make serious assumptions about features of the environment that are relevant to birds, assumptions which have not been made sufficiently explicit nor tested. This last point requires emphasis, for if we are interested in describing the physical environment or substrate so as to relate its structure and complexity to the diversity of animals occupying it, our description must focus on features relevant to the animals in question. An aquarium that is perfectly uniform except for thermal stratification from top to bottom will be either homogeneous or not to the organisms introduced therein, depending upon whether these organisms perceive or in some manner respond to the temperature differences in the different layers. Von Uexküll (1921) has popularized this notion of the "relevant environment" or *Umwelt*, i.e., the environment as perceived by the organism, as distinct from the whole environment. A useful measure of environmental heterogeneity must, therefore, take into account the animal's *Umwelt* and need not concern itself with other environmental elements. This implies that for each class of animals —i.e., each group with different sensory capacities—a different description of the habitat may be required. A description relevant to the *Umwelt* of birds, for whom vision is the dominant modality, could be irrelevant to an olfactorily oriented fossorial rodent. Fortunately, there appears to be a strong correlation between the features of the environment that make up the *Umwelt* of birds and those on which the *Umwelt* of mammals, reptiles, and insects depend. We cannot yet be certain of this, but one description will possibly suffice for all species. Certainty (or rejection) must wait until adequate censuses of mammals, reptiles, amphibia, and insects are available, censuses comparable to those presently available for birds (for a few species) which allow direct comparisons of the species diversities of these different classes.

Rather than summarize all measurable features of environments, we can suppose that the variety of certain features can be correlated with species diversity. One method of correlation is to calculate a multiple regression coefficient of bird species diversity against all the measures of habitat diversity which might be deemed appropriate. The "guesses" or hypotheses concerning which factors can be profitably compared need not be wild speculations: an experienced naturalist has a keen sense of what is likely to be relevant to a bird. For instance, one "guess" was that the controlling environmental feature was the profile of the foliage; the accuracy of this guess should not be attributed solely to serendipity! Let us look more closely at this notion of profile. It is possible to make a vertical section through a wood and calculate the total volume or density of the foliage. One can then graph the proportion of the total foliage, at any level, against height. Such a graph for a field, a spruce wood, and a deciduous wood is given in Figure 2–2. (Note that these graphs do not depend on actual counts of leaves or leaf volumes.) Several more accurate and much easier techniques for such assays are available, e.g., measuring the horizontal distance from a point that a standard-sized plate must be moved before one half of its area is obscured, or that percentage of sky obscured, etc.

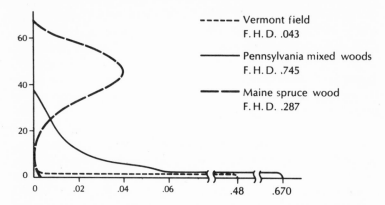

FIGURE 2–2. Some Representative Foliage Profiles and Their Foliage-Height-Diversity Indices. (Based on MacArthur and MacArthur, 1961.)

(see MacArthur and MacArthur, 1961). One can arbitrarily divide the vertical axis of the graph into layers—in practice, three layers comprising the vertical distances 0 to 2 feet, 2 to 25 feet, and over 25 feet seem easiest to handle (and correspond best to the natural division of grass, shrubs, and trees), although other divisions could be used. It is then possible to calculate the proportion of the total foliage that falls into each of these layers, from which we can derive a foliage height diversity index, $P_i \log_e P_i$, where P_1 now becomes the proportion of the total foliage present in layer i. The empirical result with data from a variety of areas in the eastern United States is a remarkable fit, with bird species diversity = 2.01 × foliage height diversity + .46. Interestingly, knowledge of the actual plant species, i.e., plant species diversity, does not improve our knowledge of bird species diversity.

The predictive value of the foliage diversity index can be illustrated in yet another way. The proportions of foliage in the three horizontal layers of a wood can be indicated by a point in a triangle (see Figure 2–3) where the distance of the point from each side is proportional to the fraction of the foliage found in a given layer. If one knows the habitat preferences of particular species of birds, one should then be able to predict whether those species will be found in a given area. When the prediction is not sustained, the implication will be that some other requirement is absent, i.e., that the foliage profiles are not a sufficient description of the habitat. This is true for a minority of species, but, happily, not true for most. Note, too, that this does not mean that birds actually perceive and select habitats on the basis of foliage densities, but merely that the vertical distribution of different densities of leaves is correlated with both bird species diversity and particular foliage profiles with the presence of particular species. We shall return to this point in the next chapter.

It must be made explicit that quantitative relationships between the diversity of an environment and a species inhabiting it has been thus far described largely for birds. However, comparable data for lizards (Pianka, personal communication) will soon become available. Thus, we can hope that a more general theorem may someday emerge. However, it is also possible that we will have to content ourselves with a different set of specifications for every class of organism—with the measure of environmental diversity as it applies to beetles being quite different than that for butterflies. Hoping that nature does allow broad generalizations, let us continue our examination of patterns of diversity even though we know that the guidelines are drawn almost entirely from studies of birds.

On Bird Species Diversity: The Tropics

In the northeastern United States MacArthur's formula allows a prediction of bird species diversity on the basis of a measure of foliage height diversity. Does the formula apply elsewhere? A pre-

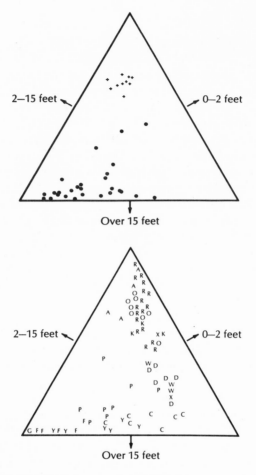

FIGURE 2–3. The Relation between Habitat Type and the Presence of Certain Species. The first triangle indicates the proportion of foliage in three horizontal layers in two different habitats: the crosses represent second growth forest, the dots a brushy field. The fraction of the total foliage in each layer is proportionate to the length of a line normal to each of the triangle's sides.

The second triangle indicates, in the same fashion, the foliage height distribution in several different habitats where particular birds occur: each letter indicates a different species. By superimposing two such graphs and noting which species of birds are found in particular kinds of habitats, reasonably accurate predictions as to which species will be present can be made from foliage data alone. (Based on MacArthur, MacArthur, and Preer, 1962.)

liminary analysis (Klopfer and MacArthur, 1961) suggested it required a modification before it could be applied to the tropics. That is, for a given value of foliage height diversity the species diversity of tropical habitats appeared to be greater than those which would have been predicted for a temperate zone habitat. Since the richness of tropical faunas has often been remarked upon, this finding came as no surprise. Whether one studies birds or beetles, trees or toads, the variety of forms increases sharply as one nears the equator. And this sharpness of increase in variety as one approaches latitude 0 is of major significance for the argument that tropical diversity is not a diffusion phenomenon. For instance, if most species originate in the tropics, or if the pace of evolution is somehow accelerated in the tropics, there should be a clinal increase in species diversity or number of species as one proceeds toward the equator. Not only do bird censuses fail to show a smooth incline—the number of breeding birds suddenly doubles between southern Texas and northern Central America—but different families show marked differences in their relative abundance. In general, the nonpasserine species (as opposed to the Passeriformes, the order of "perching birds") are more abundant in the tropics than elsewhere, a fact which weakens any simple diffusion-from-the-tropics hypothesis.

A number of other explanations for the greater diversity of the tropics have been considered. For instance, it is possible that the tropics have a more extensive history of freedom from disturbance and have more species within them simply because of their greater antiquity as compared with other areas. However, recent evidence does not support this hypothesis. The glacial epochs, which are presumed to be the major causes of pleistocene extinctions, would have merely shifted ecological zones latitudinally, not eliminated them. Moreover, pleistocene climatic changes would be most pronounced at the poles and in the tropics: the already variable temperate climates would have been least affected (for details see Connell and Orias, 1964). Another explanation for the diversity of the tropics is found in the theory that there are more "niches" in the tropics and thus more species (by "niche" is meant the constellation of factors which determines the *Umwelt* of the species). However, it is not possible to enumerate the number of niches *a priori*, that is, one cannot look at the physical structure of an area and predict how many niches exist within it. The dimensions of a niche are in large part defined by the presence of other species; therefore, adding another species to a community alters the niches of other species in a manner that substrate analysis cannot predict. A variant of this "more niches" concept is that the tropical areas are floristically more heterogeneous or complex and thus provide a greater number of ways in which the substrate can be subdivided. This idea cannot be wholly rejected, although it does beg the question as to why the floras of tropical regions are more diverse than those elsewhere. Further, it does not account for the fact that, at least in birds, the increase in diversity is not attended by equal changes in abundance among all families. As has been mentioned, passerines and nonpasserines change their abundance differentially (Klopfer and MacArthur, 1960, 1961). (Of course, this fact could have an entirely separate explanation.)

Yet another tropical diversity is based upon energetic considerations (Connell and Orias, 1964). The hypothesis is that there is increased production in tropical regions, due to less energy being needed for maintenance, which may be manifested either by the individual organism growing faster and decreasing the age at which it attains sexual maturity or by an increase in the rate of offspring production. An increased number of individuals presumably allows for more genetic diversity and greater opportunity for the formation of new species. However, this is probably not the case in birds which, in the tropics, take longer to mature than they do in temperate regions, generally have smaller clutches, and probably suffer far more losses from predators than their northern counterparts. Increased productivity certainly does have relevance to the problem of species diversity, but it probably operates primarily to allow for the continued existence of "marginal" species (MacArthur, 1965). As for the possibility that capability for breeding any time of year contributes to diversity, that, too, must be rejected. The average length of the breeding season of individual species is proportionately the same whatever the length of the total breeding season (Ricklefs, 1966), that is, if the overall breeding season is doubled, so is the average duration of each species' breeding season. Differences in the timing of breeding are therefore not responsible for tropical diversity.

This author has suggested that while the constancy of the tropical climate is a relevant factor, it exerts its influence by allowing a greater degree of specialization (Klopfer, 1962, 1965). This statement is based upon two premises, already mentioned: (1) there is a limit to the degree of similarity that two coexisting (sympatric) species can show, and (2) every species will adopt the least costly or more efficient technique available to it for the extraction of energy from the environment. Where climatic conditions are unstable, or the sources of food and cover variable, the degree of specialization a bird can afford must, necessarily, be less than where constant climatic conditions prevail. For example, a tropical bird will generally become accustomed to one kind of food or one kind of tree, but a year-round resident of more northern regions must face a somewhat different environment winter, spring, summer, and fall. Thus, constancy of conditions permits a greater degree of specialization or behavioral stereotypy in tropical birds as compared with the necessarily more versatile jacks-of-all-trades of the temperate zones, and this greater specialization, in turn, causes an increase in the maximum degree of similarity that can be tolerated between coexisting species. A community of specialists can have more noncompeting members than a community of more versatile members. Experimental tests of stereotypy in perceptual preferences and feeding of tropical and temperate zone birds have not fully supported this hypothesis (Klopfer, 1965, 1967). It has been found that at least some tropical species, although normally stereotyped in their behavior and limited in their occurrences, are fully capable of expansion into new environmental areas and utilization of new modes of feeding; they are not specialists because of any basic inability to be more versatile. The banana quit of Central America is a case in point: usually restricted to the forest edge of flower gardens, and very restricted in the motor patterns it utilizes for feeding, this bird behaves quite differently on the Caribbean islands which it inhabits. In Puerto Rico, for instance, it is one of the most common birds in virtually every habitat but grasslands and cane fields. It is seen in situations using feeding techniques, which, on the mainland, are unknown. This is a good example of the theory that the apparent stereotypy of tropical birds may be a result rather than a cause of a high species diversity.

Strategies other than increasing stereotypy may also increase the limiting similarity of coexisting species. For example, by increasing the productivity of the habitat, i.e., the total amount of available energy (provided there is no corresponding decrease in the spectrum of resources whose productivity is increased), or by reducing the resource requirements (by decreases in mortality and therefore in clutch size), the species diversity could also be increased. As indicated above, an increase in habitat productivity is effective to the degree that it will allow formerly marginal habitats to become adequate to sustain productive life; low reproductive rates, not adverse where death rates are low and stable, may reduce energetic requirements. And each of these features also applies to the tropics. Hence, the increased diversity of the tropics need not be attributed to a single cause (MacArthur, 1965).

On Bird Species Diversity: Islands

Although species diversity is greater in tropical regions than in temperate areas, islands, wherever they occur, are faunistically impoverished as compared with adjacent mainland areas. Why is this so?

Islands, being generally smaller in area than the adjoining mainland, will have a reduced number of the different kinds of habitat available. Hence, the total species diversity of an island would be expected to be less than that of a comparably sized piece of mainland. However, even within a single habitat (e.g., grassland), islands will be relatively depauperate. This is often attributed to the difficulty of colonization when open ocean must be bridged. Thus on Pacific islands (the Moluccas, Melanesia, and Oceania) one finds a decrease in the number of fresh water and terrestrial bird species as a function of the distance from New Guinea, the primary source of the colonists (MacArthur and Wilson, 1963). The usual assumption has been that, given adequate time, island habitats would eventually contain as many species as comparable mainland habitats: only the overall island diversity would remain low compared with the mainland (this is referred to as the "between-habitat diversity"). The "within-habitat diversities" would eventually be the same in islands as on the mainlands.

Actually, this is probably never true, even for islands lying close to a mainland shore, such as Trinidad. One reason is that just as an island can gain species through immigration, so can it lose species through extinction. For example, imagine an island being colonized by an ever-increasing sample of species from the mainland. Since no species will restrict its habitat unless compelled to do so, the first arrivals will occupy all appropriate areas, i.e., a wider selection of habitats than on the mainland where competition forces restrictions upon each species. As other species arrive, the early arrivals will be faced with increased interspecific competition, which, since there is a limit to the similarity of coexisting species, can only be resolved by a progressive restriction in habitats. But, eventually, because of the size of the island, no further habitat division will be possible. If one fourth of an acre of grassland is necessary to support one pair of seed-eaters, and if the island contains but one eighth of an acre of grass, the seed-eaters may survive only as long as they can also exploit the forest edge. Once the arrival of specialized forest-edge species occurs, the seed-eaters will become extinct; the limited size of their island will have effectively negated the existence of the grassland.

Multiple regression analyses of environmental correlates of insular bird species abundance implicate area as the major predictor of species numbers (Hamilton et al., 1964). For plants elevation appears to be the major determinant of the number of species; area may be relevant only to species the individual numbers of which are regulated by density-dependent means. In addition, as the number of species increases the number of each kind that can be supported will decrease. The fewer the number of individuals of each species, the greater the probability that a chance event or natural catastrophe will eliminate the species altogether. In short, although islands have a steady rate of colonization, they also have a rate of extinction. Colonization cannot lead to an infinite increase in diversity, for at some point an equilibrium between colonization and extinction will be reached.

The argument that insufficiency of time for colonization and breeding is largely responsible for the depauperate condition of islands is further belied by the following example. The island of Krakatau in the Pacific, which lost all of its vertebrate fauna (and probably most invertebrates as well) in a volcanic explosion in 1883, had reconstituted its fauna within fifty years (Dammermann, 1948). By the mid-twentieth century, the birds and mammals of Krakatau were comparable to those of undisturbed islands of sim-

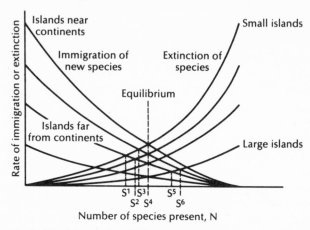

FIGURE 2–4. The MacArthur-Wilson Model for Explaining the Number of Species on an Island. Immigration rates are inversely proportional to the distance of an island from a large continental source of colonists; extinction rates are inversely proportional to size. Hence, the actual number of species at equilibrium will vary according to the interaction between these two factors, as indicated by this graph. (Based on MacArthur and Wilson, 1963.)

ilar size and remoteness. Thus, it appears that initial colonization may proceed very quickly, indeed, and it seems unlikely that the passage of time alone will appreciably increase the species diversity of Krakatau.

The equilibrium theory of insular diversity (MacArthur and Wilson, 1963) is illustrated by Figure 2–4, which is intended to imply, among other things, (1) that islands more distant from the source of supply of new species will have a lower colonization rate than those less distant; (2) smaller islands will have a greater extinction rate than larger islands; and (3) on distant islands, an increase in area will have a greater effect on the number of species than on less distant islands (note the difference in the slopes of the immigration and extinction curves). The equilibrium value of the number of species present is obviously fixed by the intersection of the lines representing immigration and extinction, a value that is less than that of comparable mainland areas largely because of the reduced between-habitat diversity. The behavioral implications of this fact will be considered in the next chapter.

Summary

The earth is a highly heterogeneous planet—an obvious fact of physiography, but one with considerable ramifications. The existence of patchworks of different habitats allows for the coexistence of different species. Were the environment uniform, interspecific competition would be heightened and the total number of different species inevitably reduced. Attempts to describe and enumerate the habitats of the earth in a quantitative fashion have generally proven less than useful; one of the major reasons is that descriptions of the environment, if they are to be used to predict the occurrence and abundance of animals, must be related to the environment as actually perceived by an animal (its *Umwelt*). A different set of criteria and description will possibly be required for different groups of animals.

In the case of birds, species diversity appears most closely related to the diversity of the foliage height distribution. Tropical regions and islands, however, are exceptional in that the former have unduly rich and the latter unduly impoverished faunas. The richness of the tropics is probably due to their greater climatic stability which permits exploitation of marginal habitats, and it may be partially due to increased specialization (in terms of behavioral stereotypy), made advantageous by the possibility of relying on the same kind of food and cover throughout the year. Islands are relatively impoverished largely because of their small size, which leads to a reduction in the between-habitat diversity.

3

THE SELECTION
OF HABITATS

THE EASE with which experienced naturalists can locate a particular species of animal is due to each animal's fairly specific preferences for a particular habitat and to the naturalist's acumen for recognizing the relevant characteristics of that habitat. Thus, animals with sensory abilities and a perceptual world which are akin to our own may be easily located. Even most city dwellers would not look for woodpeckers in a pasture, nor for albatrosses in a cedar bog. However, knowing where to search for an empiid fly, or a coelacanth fish requires more esoteric knowledge. In this chapter we shall focus upon how animals define or perceive their environment, the processes involved in the development of particular preferences for particular habitats, and the stability of those preferences once they are established. We shall generally be considering *proximate causes* (a phrase coined by Lack [1954] although the underlying notion stems from Aristotle). To explain, it is generally accepted that causability operates at more than one level. For example, the factor that initiates the southward migration of northern songbirds is known to be a change in length of day, which is the immediately disposing condition or *proximate cause*. However, any birds failing to migrate would be unlikely to survive the winter, and this factor represents a historic or *ultimate cause* of autumnal migration. The ultimate, or evolutionary, explanations for habitat selection should be apparent from the discussion in the preceding chapter.

The Umwelt *of the Animal*

In experimental studies of psychological preferences we dare not take for granted that the perceptual world of the animal subject and the student are identical, especially when sensory capacities differ radically. Certain fish can detect disturbances in the electric fields they produce around themselves (Lissman, 1958); bees can visually perceive ultraviolet rays, which we cannot see (Von Frisch, 1965); bats apparently construct pictures of their surroundings from high-frequency echoes (Griffin, 1958); and many species of animals possess olfactory capabilities that create an entire world to which we are denied admission. Jakob von Uexküll (1921) was among the first to elaborate the theme that the differences in the perceptual worlds of animals may result in their treating seemingly identical environments in quite different ways. The *Umwelt,* the environment as perceived, of an eyeless mole, an earthworm, and a burrowing owl, differs radically, even though the burrows of these creatures may lie side by side. Similarly, a bird that occupies what appear to us to be two different kinds of habitat may, in fact, be choosing habitats on the basis of cues that are common to both sides.

But how can one determine the character of the *Umwelt?* One approach is through direct neurophysiological or physiological investigations of sensory abilities. For instance, it has been possible to record the output of small groups of retinal cells of frogs and pigeons and, by controlling the stimuli presented to the eye, to pinpoint the characteristics to which the receptors respond. Some retinal units or groups of cells proved sensitive to convex edges moving across the visual field, others to changes in light intensity, and so on (Maturana *et al.,* 1960). Using cats and a similar technique, but varying the wavelength of the light being presented, Granit first raised the possibility that these animals see colors (Granit, 1955). Previously cats had been assumed to be color-blind.

Panel 1

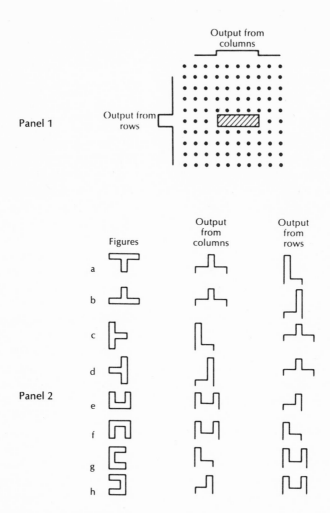

Panel 2

FIGURE 3–1. Illustration of a Hypothesis by Sutherland (see Wells, 1962) of Shape Discrimination in the Octopus. In panel 1 the small dots represent an array of cells of the retina. A horizontally oriented rectangle is projected onto the retina (shaded area) and produces a patterned output from the columns and rows that is represented by the two graphs on the edge of the array. Panel 2 illustrates the column and row outputs for a variety of other figures. In panel 3 the outputs

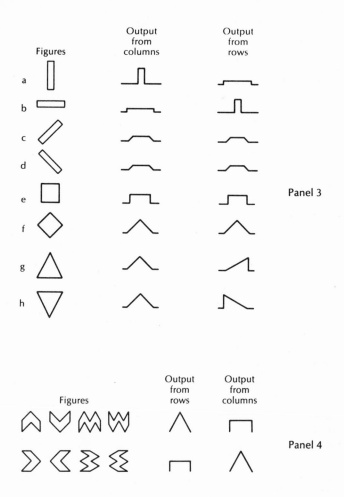

for pairs of mirror images are shown, and panel 4 contains figure-pairs whose row-column outputs are indistinguishable. The hypothesis predicts that visual discrimination is possible for the octopus only between figures whose "outputs" differ, i.e., in panel 2, c and d should be indistinguishable, but not b and c. Any two figures on any one line in panel 4 should be indistinguishable as well. (Based on Sutherland, 1960.)

Another study has shown that when electrodes tap the gustatory nerves of a rat's tongue, to which measured concentrations of particular solutions can then be applied, the ability to discriminate different "flavors" can be observed (Pfaffman, 1955; Erickson, 1963). However, a drawback to this approach is that it is difficult to determine whether the animal actually employs the information provided by his peripheral receptors. It is one thing to know that a bird does possess a differential peripheral sensitivity to various wavelengths of light, but it is another to demonstrate that this ability is relevant to its daily behavior, rather than a useless vestige of an ancestral trait. This problem can be surmounted by requiring the animal to make one response in the presence of a particular stimulus (e.g., a red light), and to make another response, or no response, to a different stimulus (e.g., an orange light). The stimuli are then progressively modified so as to become increasingly similar. The point at which discrimination breaks down can then be easily determined. For instance, Figure 3–1 depicts sets of visual patterns that an octopus can and cannot learn to discriminate among, and provides similar information for tactile patterns. From these studies we can learn a great deal about how these creatures organize their environment through their perceptions.

A second approach to the analysis of an *Umwelt* is based upon the measurement of overt preferences in artificial, "simplified" environments in which but a single feature is varied at a time. This has been recently attempted with insects, lizards, mice, and birds (e.g., Harris, 1952; Sexton *et al.,* 1964; Klopfer, 1962, 1963, 1967). In the studies with birds, individuals were first either hand-reared or habituated to aviary confinement, and then released singly into chambers divided by netting into two equal sections. Artificial perches were equally distributed about the chamber, light intensity was either held constant or varied consistently, and internal partitions either allowed or prevented simultaneous visual access to both compartments of the chamber. Artificial foliage was symmetrically arranged on the perches and was varied with regard to size, shape, and leaf density. The birds were free to move from one compartment to the other through a connecting channel within which food was available at any time. Movement through the channel activated timers, providing a constant measure of the time spent by the bird in the different "habitats" (see Figure 3-2). It was shown that for some species of birds leaf shape and size are, indeed, irrelevant, but light intensity and the distribution of patches of shadow are relevant cues (the latter was true for a sparrow inhabiting scrubby brush and undergrowth, the wintering white-throated sparrow). Other species of birds appeared to discriminate between size, shape, and density of foliage.

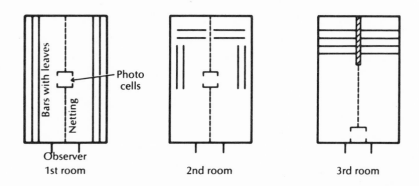

FIGURE 3-2. Floorplans of Klopfer's Leaf-Preference Test Chambers. The varied arrangements to which all birds were subjected assured that any bias shown by the birds was due to the differences in the foliage in the opposite sides of the chamber, and not to idiosyncrasies of any one chamber. The birds fed in the vestibule, in which photocells monitored their movements from one side to the other. Each time a bird fed, it had to select its "habitat" anew.

Although studies utilizing artificial environments provide some information about an animal's *Umwelt,* the very simplicity of these environments may be self-defeating. The fact that a chipping sparrow prefers pine foliage to oak when perching opportunities, food availability, and temperature are equal is of limited relevance to natural situations in which no such equality will occur. Pine trees generally provide fewer lateral perches per unit volume than oaks; and they harbor different insects, and they provide less complete protection (in summer) from wind and rain. Experiments could be performed in which several variables are simultaneously manipulated, but the time and effort needed would be prohibitive. Only when the number of relevant environmental variables is relatively small can we expect informative results from studies of preference that include attention to interactive effects.

A third method of dealing with the problem of *Umwelt* definition was alludèd to in Chapter 1 (see Bibliography, MacArthur, 1965, and MacArthur *et al,* various dates). To recapitulate briefly, it was originally supposed that species diversity (in this case, of birds) is correlated with the diversity in the density of foliage at different heights. Species diversity was defined as $-p_i\log_e p_i$, and foliage height diversity was similarly obtained after arbitrarily dividing the foliage into three layers of 0 to 2 feet, 2 to 15 feet, and over 15 feet, and measuring the proportion of the total foliage that comprised each layer. The bird species diversity of various northeastern habitats was found to bear the following relation to the foliage height diversity:

$$BSD = 2.01 \; FHD + .46.$$

Various other subdivisions of the foliage profile were proposed, for there is nothing biological about 0 to 2 feet, 2 to 15 feet, and over 15 feet; some subdivisions gave a less linear relation. Distinguishing a greater number of layers increased the complexity of the calculations without yielding a commensurate gain in accuracy. It was then demonstrated that the residual scatter after partial regression of bird species diversity on foliage height diversity is not accounted for by variations in *plant species* diversity or (in the north temperate zone) by latitude. This does not necessarily mean that birds perceive differences in foliage height diversity. However, an interesting insight was provided when the data were regraphed in the form of triangles (see Figure 3–3, p. 47), each side of which represented one of the three layers into which the foliage of a given habitat was divided. Any given habitat could then be represented by a point the perpendicular distance of which from each of the three sides is proportional to the proportion of the total foliage in each of the three respective layers. Now, one can independently identify the various species of birds found in a given habitat and indicate their presence on the same triangle, as in Figure 3–3 (see

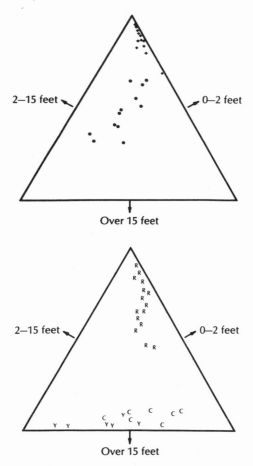

FIGURE 3–3. Various Species of Birds Found in a Given Habitat. Each side of these two equilateral triangles represents foliage at one of three arbitrarily selected levels: 0 to 2 feet, 2 to 15 feet, and over 15 feet. The proportions of the foliage of any given site that fall into one of these layers are indicated by the distance from the appropriate side on a line drawn perpendicularly to that side. In the first triangle the foliage composition of several dense second growth forest sites (+) and of old field sites (·) are plotted. The second diagram indicates the characteristics of the habitat in which individuals of three species of bird were found: C = yellow-breasted chat, R = red-eyed vireo, and Y = Maryland yellowthroat. (Based on MacArthur *et al.*, 1962.)

also Chapter 2, p. 32). This figure indicates that catbirds, for example, are found where the foliage is predominately in the 2- to 15-feet layer, while red-eyed vireos are located where the bulk of the foliage is greater than 15 feet in height. Armed with such general knowledge of the different species' habitat choices and with the foliage height diversity of a particular area, one can make a rough prediction of an area's census. Again, this does not demonstrate that the bird selects an area by perception of foliage height differences, but that particular foliage height diversities can be correlated with the presence or absence of particular species. Further, as long as this is the best correlation known, it is fair to assume that foliage height diversities are, in fact, perceived and responded to, at least by birds of North America. As will be evident, most of the generalizations on perception, the *Umwelt*, and habitat selection have had to be based on an embarrassingly impoverished sample!

The MacArthur technique, described above, is admittedly the least direct of the approaches to studies of the *Umwelt*. At the same time, its predictive power has proven sufficiently great to warrant its continued and intensified use. By a series of approximations an ever better set of correlations between the presence of particular species and the characteristics of the environment may be obtained. From these data one may yet be able to deduce the character of the environment as perceived and selected by the organism.

Experimental Studies of Habitat Selection

How does an animal come to prefer a particular habitat? Can preferences, once established, be changed? How readily will second-best choices be accepted? These and a host of related questions have yet to be answered for a single species. The two illustrations that follow merely provide an example of how such work is being pursued (one is by Wecker, 1963; the other by Klopfer and Hailman, 1965).

The prairie and forest races of the Michigan deermouse are ecologically segregated. As implied by their common names, the one subspecies is found in woods, the other in fields. Mice of the two types were obtained either by live trapping or from a stock that had been laboratory reared under thoroughly unnatural conditions for more than a dozen generations. The testing procedure was to measure (by automatically monitored treadles) the amount of time individual mice spent in varying portions of a 1,600-square-foot enclosure, half of which enclosed a woods (the normal habitat of the woodland race), and half a field (home of the prairie subspecies). The instrumentation allowed separate analyses of the time the deermouse spent actively moving about the field or woods, the time spent in nesting in the two areas, and rates of movement and depth of penetration into the two habitats. The variables that Wecker manipulated were heredity (offspring of field or laboratory parents) and early experience (whether the mice were reared in field, wood, or laboratory).

The results are represented, in part, in Figure 3–4. They may be interpreted as follows: regular choice of the field over the woods environment by young of the prairie race does occur whether the young are reared in the lab or the field or the woods, and field rearing does appear to strengthen this preference. Laboratory stock derived from field-dwelling mice are more malleable: if laboratory reared they prefer fields, but if woods reared, their woods preference is not statistically significant. Apparently, the confinement to laboratory conditions for 12 to 20 generations has reduced the degree of genetic control over responses to the appropriate habitat. In the normally reared mice, early experience serves to activate the perceptual preferences characteristic of the strain.

To study the development of habitat preferences in the chipping sparrow, a basic design similar to Wecker's was used. First, the foliage preferences of adult birds were determined. These birds had been captured in the wild but had been habituated to the conditions of captivity. The experimental conditions were as described earlier (p. 44). The habitat preference shown by the chipping sparrow was for pine needles over oak leaves, and the control subjects were birds that had been hand-reared as a group from an early age (before their eyes opened) in a room devoid of foliage. A third group was hand-reared in the presence of oak leaves, the foliage least preferred by the birds captured in the wild. Preference tests of these last two groups were conducted after the birds reached two months in age and were repeated at intervals thereafter. After the first test,

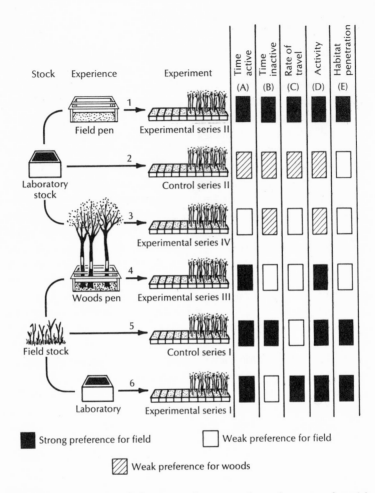

FIGURE 3–4. Summary of Observations reveals preferences of prairie deermice from various backgrounds. (From Stanley C. Wecker, "Habitat Selection." Copyright © 1964 by Scientific American, Inc. All rights reserved.)

all birds, including those reared apart from any foliage, were housed in large outdoor aviaries which afforded the sight of pine trees overhead and on all sides, but contained only broad-leafed trees (oaks and dogwoods). The preference tests were performed in a manner previously described (p. 44), with both natural and artificial foliage being used (Klopfer and Hailman, 1965; Klopfer,

1962). The results showed a marked preference for pine among the birds captured in the wild as well as among those birds reared without any foliage. The birds reared in the presence of oak leaves, however, showed a pronounced shift in preference: some individuals strongly preferred oak over pine; some showed a strong preference for pine over oak. However, as these birds matured, their preference for pine increased, and birds which, before maturity, had preferred oak, at twelve months of age selected pine. Thus, visual experience with the usually preferred foliage was sufficient to overcome the effects of the rearing experience.

However, we must emphasize that preferences for particular types or shapes of leaves represent only a fragment of the preferences that determine total habitat choice. In these experiments, variables such as perching opportunities, kind and distribution of food, and light and shadow patterns and intensities were held constant. Nevertheless, in the absence of other variables, these experiments appear to demonstrate that for these birds, as with field mice, there are perceptual biases that are relatively stable, although capable of temporary modification. The how and why of the shifts to the normal preferences of the species shown by the oak reared birds will have to be answered by further study.

Habitat Correlation: Selection by External Agents

Imagine yourself playing marbles on a sandy beach. Suppose you were to begin your game with a large collection of marbles of every possible color. On completing your game you might find that some marbles had been lost, and more likely than not, a disproportionate number of those lost would have been of the tawny, gray, or duller shades. The marbles themselves cannot show any preference for the sandy beach over your pockets, but, by virtue of your being better able to detect those with colors contrasting to the color of the sand, your marbles might appear to have color-correlated habitat preferences. You, the player, were exerting a selection pressure, and the marbles themselves made no choices. Thus a correlation between an organism and a particular habitat is not necessarily evidence that the organism has selected its habitat. Such a correlation is called *habitat correlation,* not *habitat selection.*

The downy young of some seabirds match the substrate upon which they hatch. On dark beaches, more dark young exist, and on light beaches, more light. The young, of course, do not select their birthplaces, although their parents may. Perhaps parental selection of nesting sites accounts for color correlation. Or, predators may be quick to detect and remove chicks of contrasting colors, generally leaving the better camouflaged ones for the naturalist to count. The relative power of predators in such circumstances has been compellingly revealed by an Englishman (Kettlewell, 1959, 1965) who placed dark- and light-colored individuals of a particular species of moth on the soot-covered trunks of trees. The dark or melanic moths were well concealed on the dark background, and most of them remained untouched by predators. Interestingly, there is no evidence that the moths select a color-matched background to light on. This particular example of apparent habitat selection, which is really another case of mere habitat correlation, has been of particular interest to biologists because, in England, the proportion of melanic individuals of several species of moths has risen steadily since the mid-nineteenth century. Their rise has been well documented, due to the fortunate circumstance that many English clergymen catch butterflies and moths. The rise in the numbers of melanics is apparently causally correlated with the increased deposition of soot on England's green countryside following industrialization and the widespread use of coal. With improved control over soot production, and the restoration of more pristine conditions, it is predicted that the number of melanics will gradually decrease.

Note that although there is no evidence to show that these moths themselves choose a background to match their color, they do orient themselves with their long axis parallel to the vertical ridges of the bark, thus rendering themselves least conspicuous. (For illustrations of the remarkable degree to which such matching may occur, see Cott [1940] whose work is an impressive contribution to the study of mimicry and camouflage, a facsimile of one such matching appearing in Figure 3–5). This orientation is actually performed by each individual moth and is in this instance not due to predators having removed all those not properly oriented. Here, then, the habitat correlation (i.e., alignment of body axis and back ridges) is due to a response of the animal, and not the action of an external agent. Of course, that agent, the predatory bird, probably represents the ultimate cause for the development of the orienting response in the first place. We may further assume that eventually a mutant moth will choose a tree with bark of a shade similar to its own. This moth and its successors will be better protected than its

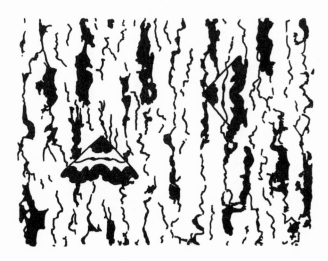

FIGURE 3–5. Illustration of How the Alignment of a Moth on a Tree Trunk May Render It Either Cryptic or Conspicuous. (Based on Cott, 1940.)

predecessors. Indeed, any moth or snail that places itself or its eggs on a substrate matching in color or texture will be likely to make a greater genetic contribution to succeeding generations than those failing to exercise such a choice. Even if the increase in survival is but a fraction of 1 per cent, this percentage will increase over time. Thus, given nonrandom predation or differential selection of prey on the basis of substrate matching, such evolutionary accommodation will eventually occur. The predator then becomes the ultimate rather than the proximate cause of the habitat correlation and true habitat selection will have occurred.

Although Kettlewell's studies (op. cit.) of protective coloration may be the best known, it was preceded by many others, including experimental studies of the value of color matching for protection from predators in fish, insects, and artificial models (Sumner, 1935; Turner, 1961). The fact that so many animals such as various species of bottom-dwelling flatfish and lizards can change color so as to continually match their background attests to the powerful selective advantage of visual camouflage. Nor does this mean that color matching is the most important kind of camouflage, since the effectiveness of color matching is largely dependent on color vision being present and relevant to the predator. (We will return to this point later.) The main point to be stressed is that some instances of apparent habitat selection are due to no more than the immediate action of an external agent, such as a predator. Only when this pressure produces a preference for a particular habitat by an animal can one truly speak of habitat selection. Whenever a situation of apparent habitat selection does exist, however, one may expect natural selection ultimately to alter the population to include individuals who exercise some choice. The cues on which this choice or habitat selection is based may be remote from the cues necessary to the predator and this adds to the investigator's problems. For example, we know that thrushes of Cambridgeshire preferentially prey on snails the color and banding patterns of which distinguish them to the greatest degree on the ground. This fact has been established quantitatively because thrushes in the relatively flat, rockless countryside of East Anglia (and elsewhere) carry their snails to conspicuous rocks to crush and devour them; these "thrush anvils" thus provide a means for a census of snails captured. The dominant color of the captured snails varies seasonally, as does the color of the substrate. After the death of the summer's growth of grass, the green-hued snails are more conspicuous than they are when cloistered in the verdant growth (Cain and Sheppard, 1954; Goodhart, 1958). However, other evidence suggests differences in the responsiveness of snails of different color phases to various temperatures. Those snails that are better color-matched in the summer may also be less active; their heightened vulnerability in the winter may be due to increased activity as much as to the diminished value of their camouflage. Or consider the following example. Amid the white sands of the southwestern United States are islands of black lava. Races of mice inhabiting the "islands" have dark pelage, those on the sand are light in color. Do the mice select appropriate habitats? Or are they selected by their predators? The primary predators of these small rodents are snakes, which depend very little on visual cues for tracking mice. But as long as other, visually oriented, predators discriminate the slightest bit in favor of the better matched individuals, the pelage-substrate correlation can be maintained without any habitat selection by individual mice. Is this actually the case? Empirical evidence for individual choices would not be difficult to obtain (see Wecker, 1963), but, for such a case, only speculations are possible at the present time.

Of course, it is not only predators that may selectively remove one class of organisms from a habitat. Climatic factors may operate in a similar manner, e.g., extreme cold can affect certain species, or varieties, more than others (see Hilden, 1965). Thus, the migratory behavior of the Ortolan finch, and its absence in the yellow bunting finch, can be correlated with differences in thermal sensitivity: the Ortolan is more sensitive to cold (Wallgren, 1954; a detailed review of climatic effects is in Hilden, 1965).

Habitat Selection through the Action of Physical Constraints

It is well known that although webbed feet may be well suited to water, they make for clumsy locomotion on land. Similarly, a parrot's beak, although cleverly designed for an animal who eats fruit or large nuts, would serve its possessor ill were he motivated to catch fish or insects. However, we must note that incredibly minor differences in form and structure may also have a major influence on the efficiency with which particular habitats, or portions of particular habitats, are exploited. As a result, these habitats may come to be preferred after the animal has had some experience both with it and with some alternate habitat. Thus, the functional test for the operation of physical constraints is that (1) initially the animal shows no particular preference, (2) it performs more efficiently in one circumstance than in another, and (3) it ultimately selects the more optimum situation.

This particular definition of a *physical constraint* allows us to distinguish *perceptual preferences,* which also depend, ultimately, on the physical organization of the central nervous system or its components. Hence, perceptual preferences, with regard to particular shapes or colors, could be considered physical constraints. Similarly, pelage-color or limited tolerances to changes in temperature can also be considered as instances of physical constraints rather than examples of selection by external agents. We cannot deny that there is common ground beneath the factors determining habitat selection. Nevertheless, it is useful to distinguish habitat correlation (i.e., selection by external agents) from the effect of physical constraints and from psychological factors. This is necessary because (1) the stability or lability may depend on the degree to which the mechanisms involved reside within or without an animal. Cases of habitat selection by external agents (habitat correlation) represent one end of a continuum; here, external agents are maximally involved, even though the organism's own makeup is far from irrelevant. At the other end of the continuum are those instances of perceptual preferences that depend largely on early experiences undergone by the individual; again, external agents are not irrelevant, but they are less immediately involved. The category under discussion, in this section, represents a midpoint: "physical constraints" are looked upon as anatomical features the characteristics of which reduce the efficiency with which one particular resource can be exploited, even while increasing the efficiency with which some other resource is exploited, thereby influencing an animal's preferences. This is analogous to the behavior of children who also come to prefer those games at which they excel. The cases in point may be obvious: the parrot's beak, mentioned above, presumably allows for a more efficient utilization of fruit than do the beak and associated musculature of a flycatcher. At the same time, however, the parrot's beak is a constraint with regard to an insectivorous habit.

Of more interest are those cases in which the differences in the anatomy of bills, legs, or other appendages are very slight, and when they are unaccompanied many other differences in size or phylogeny. For instance, the wood-edges of the Piedmont forests in North Carolina abound with small finch-like birds of generally similar proportions which presumably do not compete. Why is this so? One explanation is that these birds feed upon different foods. However, stomach analyses have revealed that for many of these birds little selection of food takes place; whatever is present is eaten, whether it be a seed or an insect. Another possibility is a diversification in feeding situations; it is possible that one species of bird feeds only above, another within, a particular bush. That such diversification does occur is now documented (MacArthur, 1958; see also Figure 1–2, p. 7). The possibility that this diversification is caused by anatomic features is strengthened by data that relate the absence of kinglets from certain birch woods to their relatively weak leg muscles (i.e., relative to similar birds such as tits, which are able to utilize birchwood perches). Perhaps the kinglet's weaker legs would be an asset in some other context; after all, constraints are relative for a given situation. As for the Carolina finch-type birds, their avoidance of competition might also be due to differences in the size or shape of the food they choose, rather than to differences in feeding efficiency related to the anatomy of their bills. This last explanation has been the subject of experimental tests (Chapter 1, Hespenheide, 1966; Hutchinson, 1959; see also Kear, 1962) which tend to confirm the important role played by structure in the shaping of function. Finally, lest it be thought these generalizations apply to birds alone, let us mention that the arboreal abilities of deermice are correlated with the length of their tails (Horner, 1954). Undoubtedly, an increasing number of other mammalian examples will become known as the studies of the complex multispecies aggregations of ungulates in Africa are completed.

Habitat Selection through the Action of Psychological Constraints

It seems that some habitat restrictions are not due to physical adaptations but to what must be termed psychological factors. The psychological preferences may be related to the ancestral habitat, or to the early experience of the individual, but whatever the cause, students of habitat selection have long agreed that subtle psychological factors often limit the distribution of a species before limits are imposed by physical tolerances or abilities (Lack and Venables, 1939; Miller, 1942; Kendeigh, 1945; Palmgren, 1949).

The experimental difficulty in studies of psychological preferences lies in demonstrating that the animal in question can utilize resources other than those generally preferred as efficiently as those which are preferred. The fact that cardinals will select millet seed when denied sunflower seeds is irrelevant if millet seeds are handled less efficiently than sunflower seeds; under conditions of competition the cardinal must necessarily revert to using the latter. In general, the preferred items are also those for which use the animal is best suited. When hand-reared chaffinches were offered a variety of seeds, preferences for particular seeds developed gradually and predictably: the birds chose those seeds which were the easiest for them to open (Kear, 1962). The most intriguing cases of psychological constraints, however, are posed by those situations in which the preferences cannot be related to physical abilities, as when a particular color of flower or shape of leaf or complex of factors is preferred to any other. Merely to identify the relevant features of a complex *Gestalt* is a problem in itself; to explain the sensory or neural basis for the preference is another matter altogether which can pose quite a challenge.

The Ontogeny of Specific Habitat Preferences

The processes whereby particular habitats or features of a habitat come to be recognized and preferred will probably not be unique to the actors; the same processes will undoubtedly be expressed in other contexts or other learning situations. Let us review those behavioral processes which seem to be most intimately involved in the establishment of habitat preferences, and then examine two experimental studies of the ontogeny of habitat selection.

Charles Darwin had accepted the notion that behavior could be classified into distinct categories labeled *learned* and *instinctive.* Learning was an adaptive modification of behavior through experience; instincts were of two kinds: The first arose spontaneously as the consequence of random genetic changes, surviving because they contributed to an increase in fitness, i.e., an ability to make a proportionately greater contribution to future generations. A duck that possessed a mutation such that it became immobile in response to creatures flying overhead would be a less likely victim of an aerial predator than its nonresponsive peers. The greater reproductive advantage entertained by such an individual would result in its mutant gene becoming progressively more common; thus, the "instinct" would become common to the species. The second kind of instincts derived from a trained response that had become habitual. Such an oft-repeated response produced (Darwin believed) physical changes in the central nervous system, and these changes altered the reproductive cells and became heritable. Darwin's theory of *pangenesis,* which proposed a mechanism for the transmission of acquired characters such as this second class of instincts, is not credible today, at least as applied to vertebrate organisms. However, Darwin's theory did imply a developmental relation between learned and instinctive behavior which *is* of current relevance.

In the century following Darwin, two separate schools of thought developed with regard to the instinct-learning dichotomy. Some experimenters such as O. Heinroth and C. O. Whitman focussed upon instinctive behavior as the more fundamental of the two, whereas others such as J. Watson focussed on behavior that was learned. The consequence of these two schools of thought was that the notion of the separateness of "knowing" and "instinct" became ever stronger. But what, in fact, is inherited? Only the zygote or fertilized egg. The formal problem is to determine how this egg interacts with its environment in such a way as to lead consistently to the appearance of particular behavior patterns. Or, as Lorenz (1965) has stated, to ask, "What are the teaching mechanisms of an animal and what do they teach him?" Thus, it is reasonable to redefine the term "instinct" so as to have it serve purely as a descriptive term, referring to behavior that normally characterizes all members of a species (or at least one sex of a species) without regard to the mechanisms that underlie that behavior. Instincts may then be characterized in terms of this plasticity, i.e., in terms of the ease with which they can be modified by experimental manipulations; they cannot be regarded as an alternative to or converse of "learned" behavior (for additional discussion of the status of the old instinct-learning controversy, see also Hinde, 1966; Marler and Hamilton, 1966; Klopfer and Hailman, 1967).

Habitat preferences are, by definition, an instance of "instinctive" behavior, in the descriptive sense proposed above. Our problem then becomes one of identifying the steps in the ontogeny of this instinct.

Morphologically Guided Learning

A child may be trained to handle his fork or crayon with either the right or left hand. For most children it is easier to learn the necessary manipulations using the right hand rather than the left; however, for a minority of children the use of the left hand is easier. It has been presumed that this difference in handedness and the related ease with which motor patterns can be learned is a function of minor structural differences in the cerebral cortex. It is, in any case, an illustration of how learning capabilities are dependent on structure, even when the structural differences can be found only at the level of nerve synapses. Grosser differences can also be involved. We have previously alluded to the fact that young birds allowed to select food from a wide assortment will at first be relatively nonselective. With increasing experience their preferences are narrowed, presumably to those seeds which they can best mandibulate. Particular bill shapes function most efficiently with certain kinds of seeds, and these seeds will thus come to be preferred (Kear, 1962; Bowman, 1961).

From an empirical point of view, it is often difficult, if not impossible, to predict the existence of some kind of morphological bias. It is rare for an organism to be, in effect, a blank slate, but to detect and define a bias may be difficult, a fact which is supported by experimental results from studies of imprinting, as explained below, which bear directly on this point.

Learning through Imprinting

The term *imprinting* should be restricted to the development of stable preferences as a consequence of an exposure to a given set of stimuli for a short period at a particular developmental state (the "critical period"; for more details see Sluckin, 1965). The tendency of salmon to return to their home streams (Hasler, 1956), the preferences of insects for particular foods or hosts (Thorpe, 1956; Hovanitz and Chang, 1963), the *Ortstreue* or return to the parental home of birds (Löhrl, 1959), or seals (R. Peterson, personal communication) may all be due to imprinting. There is also a curious instance of "avoidance" imprinting in the cabbage butterfly: rearing successive generations of its eggs on cabbage leaves *reduced* the butterfly's preference for cabbages as egg-laying sites. This response reduced the possibility of overexploiting a particular food resource, hence its particular usefulness. Notwithstanding the functional similarities of the process in such disparate groups as insects, fish, birds, and mammals, there is little reason to believe that imprinting is a unitary process involving a single neural mechanism. We should, rather, attribute similarities to the advantage conferred in certain situations by rapid, stable, one-trial learning, particularly in motorically precocial animals (see Klopfer, 1964).

Most experimental studies of imprinting have utilized domestic fowl as subjects and have exploited the fact that their newly hatched young will readily follow a large variety of objects made to move before them. Having followed an object during the first day or two of life, the young fowl will then respond to this object for many more days, being preferentially, though not exclusively, directed toward objects of the class initially presented. One particular experiment, however (originally directed toward the question of homosexuality and sexual dimorphism in ducks), revealed the existence of a subtle perceptual bias which is thus particularly relevant for inquiring into habitat preferences. In this study, newly hatched ducklings were exposed to one or other of two papier-mâché duck decoys, one plain white in color, the other symmetrically painted a variety of contrasting colors ("plain" and "painted" models). Subsequent preference tests with both models presented simultaneously gave the following results (see Figure 3–6):

1. Both "plain" and "painted" models were equally effective in eliciting a following during the initial exposure.
2. The control birds, which had not been trained but merely tested, failed to follow either model a significant number of times.

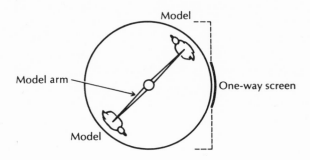

FIGURE 3–6. Bird's-eye View of Klopfer's Imprinting Chamber. A circular table of 1.5 meters diameter, it has a 20-cm.-high wall along the edge. One or two models can be presented simultaneously, with either, both, or neither outfitted with loudspeakers through which prerecorded sounds can be played. The movement of the models is controlled remotely. (Based on Klopfer, 1965.)

These two facts confirm the absence of an initial bias with regard to model preferences and the importance of an initial or training exposure as a necessary and sufficient condition for the subsequent maintenance of the following response.

3. At subsequent exposures, the experimental birds preferred the "painted" model, *irrespective of their training model.*
4. If the tests were conducted with stationary, rather than moving, models, the preference registered was for the original or training model.

It was expected that the ducklings trained with the painted model would prefer it, but it was not expected that this preference for the painted model would characterize the group trained with the plain decoy. It seemed that the act of following a decoy during the training period activated a pre-existing perceptual bias. However, one other possible explanation for these results has been offered. Perhaps the cues for recognition vary with context, one feature, color, being relevant when the models are stationary, another, e.g., dark-light edges (which would alter the degree of visual flicker induced; see James, 1959), when they are moving. An additional experiment was then conducted in which the two models differed in only one characteristic at a time—color, vertical stripedness, horizontal stripedness, etc., with preferences being tested in several situations. In some of these trials, it appeared that the ducklings could not or did not discriminate between the models; in others, their preferences accorded with predictions based on the classical notion of imprinting: upon testing they preferred the model to which they had first been exposed (Klopfer, 1967). Thus no support for the context hypothesis has been found. Note, however, that responsiveness of a duckling to the maternal call of its species is enhanced by exposure to its own brooding call (Gottlieb, 1966), an enhancement due not to stimulus generalization. Here, too, there seems to be a perceptual bias which is being activated by an *apparently* irrelevant experience.

In short, imprinting cannot be regarded as a process which can serve to develop a type of preference for any pattern, but a pre-existing bias may depend on the imprinting experience for its activation. This fact will be considered again when we turn to naturalistic studies of habitat selection, below.

Socially Guided Learning

The mere tendency of many animals to approach others of their own kind, rather than alien species, can provide a basis for maintaining a limited degree of habitat selection. This is really a form of *tradition formation,* with each generation adopting the choices of its elders not because of any intrinsic preferences but because of the attractiveness of other individuals of their species. "The innate differential in social learning" is what Howells and Vine (1940) called this tendency to approach "own kind" preferentially. It has been more recently confirmed by a study of the ontogeny of the "innate differential" (Kilham, Klopfer, and Oelke, 1968). Chicks reared in visual isolation did not prefer chicks of their own color over those of another, but if they were reared communally in the

light with their own kind, a strong preference for their "own kind"
did develop. However, similar rearing of single individuals with
several individuals of a different-color strain did not produce a
comparable preference for that strain.

Certain other instances of tradition formation have also been
documented. Black-tailed prairie dogs appear to teach their young
the laws of territorial boundaries, and these family territories remain fairly constant, even while population turnover continues
(King, 1955). In Japanese macaques (short-tailed monkeys) the
spread of particular food preferences has been chronicled as being
related to different modes of eating. For instance, on one island,
the animals wash their sweet potatoes before eating them (Miyadi,
1959).

The precise manner in which such traditional preferences
spread, or are maintained, is not yet known for primates, although
analyses of similar behavior have been made for birds. Consider
the spread of the cream-stealing habit among some English birds.
As housewives of England's isles will testify, an unprotected milk
bottle soon attracts a great tit or a blue tit, which, alighting on the
bottle, pierces the top with its bill and drinks the cream. There is
some reason to believe that the tits have learned which color tops
signify the richer milk; bottles of the less rich milk are rarely attacked when a richer alternative is available (Klopfer, unpublished
data). This habit of cream-stealing seems to have arisen spontaneously in a few widely scattered locations, spreading gradually
throughout England and then parts of Scandinavia and central
Europe, and has involved several species of birds; the specificity of
this particular mode of feeding is thus fairly broad. The spread of
the habit seems to be the result of birds being attracted to the
feeding sites of other birds; once there, they employ the feeding
techniques usual to their species. If these techniques yield cream,
the responses become re-enforced and subsequent feeding forays
will include a search for unprotected milk bottles (Fisher and
Hinde, 1950).

There have been other studies that have examined, under more
restricted conditions, the effect of one bird watching another feed
(Klopfer, 1959; Turner, 1964). In the case of one species of bird,
the European greenfinch, it was found that very few trials were

required for individual birds to learn to feed from seeds presented on one particular background and to learn not to feed on seeds presented on another. (The seeds in these experiments were from sunflowers; those forbidden to the birds had had their kernels removed and replaced with moist aspirin.) The presence of an untrained companion slowed the learning process slightly. When an untrained bird (termed an "observer") had observed the performance of a trained bird (the "actor") for some time, the former

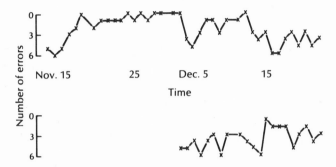

FIGURE 3–7. Learning Interference of Eating Habits by European Greenfinches. The upper curve depicts the day-to-day performance of a European greenfinch that was trained to feed from one pattern but not from another. Another bird, depicted in the lower curve, watched him perform for two weeks and was then himself trained. Not only had he not benefited from the training of his partner, but his poor performance apparently interfered with the performance of the original bird. Each X represents a series of trials held on successive days. (Based on Klopfer, 1962.)

was given an opportunity to demonstrate whether he had profited from his observations of his companion's experience. He had not. More important, once the actor had watched the observer making errors, his own performance deteriorated. Stated anthropomorphically, it was as if the trained bird, seeing a naive companion feed upon the forbidden fruit, thought, "Aha, it must be good, after all." The two birds then systematically interfered with each other's learning, each one cycling out of phase with the other (see Figure 3–7). In several cases, paired birds never discriminated consistently; there was no inhibition of incorrect responses. With a second species, the great tit, such interference did not occur. Paired birds in the same cage did not learn significantly more rapidly than single birds, but neither did they interfere with each other's learning. Since we know from their cream-stealing habit that tits are very prone to follow the lead of their flock-mates (presumably to a much greater extent than greenfinches), it is of no small importance that they are resistant to the social influences that prove so upsetting to greenfinches. It may be that the greenfinch pattern occurs in species with highly conservative feeding habits; any attempt to use a new food would be highly irregular or disadvantageous. The tit pattern would be sought among more adventuresome, exploitative feeders. Interestingly enough, among rhesus monkeys observers learn more readily when the actor errs than when he makes a correct, rewarded response (Riopelle, 1960).

For finches, however, it has been confirmed that a feeding bird is more attractive (i.e., more likely to be approached) than one that is not feeding, and that the sight of an actor feeding will induce an observer to do the same, particularly if their respective foods are close to each other. European chaffinch and common English or house sparrow observers would eat food normally unacceptable to them (because of its appearance) if they observed actors feeding upon it. Younger birds were particularly exploratory and could much more easily be induced to try unusual foods or to feed from strange receptacles. It was concluded that the main function of social feeding is to enlarge the naive bird's repertoire of foods or movements. Observations at Japanese monkey colonies (Miyadi and associates, personal communication) suggest that local habits and preferences may well have their origin in such processes, thereby adding a social dimension to the establishment of habitat preferences.

Habitat Selection and Species Diversity

We previously discussed the increased species diversity of tropical regions and the reduced diversity of islands. Among the explanations proposed for these phenomena was that tropical species, by virtue of the relative constancy of their environment, can afford a higher degree of specialization, i.e., they can exercise a finer degree of habitat selection. Let us re-examine this proposition.

A primary assumption is that tropical climates do, in fact, afford greater scope for specialization which does not require that the productivity or energy turnover of tropical regions be especially high, even though this might be the case anyway. What is required is that conditions be sufficiently uniform, and productivity sufficiently high, for an animal to restrict itself to the same year-round mode of life to a greater degree than is possible in regions which undergo distinct seasonal changes. If we grant this assumption, our experimental problem is to define and measure the actual degree of specialization shown by tropical and northern (or southern) species, preferably species of related ancestry. Additional insights can be obtained if one also examines the species inhabiting faunistically impoverished islands, especially since both particular habitats and species on islands can also be found in the adjacent mainland. Thus, a bird that is a species of honey-creeper—the banana quit— is common on the islands of Puerto Rico, Jamaica, and Dominica, as well as on the Central American mainland. However, in the latter it shares the available resources with many more species than on the islands. Can the banana quit take advantage of this reduced insular competition? Can the catbird and cardinal, species of temperate North America, expand their habitat to a greater degree when they exist on impoverished islands such as Bermuda? (See Crowell, 1961.) In short, how does the degree of habitat selectivity vary with species diversity?

An answer to this question can be found in the absence of detailed behavioral analyses of individual species (although such analyses, viz., Klopfer, 1967; Crowell, 1961; Sheppard, Klopfer, and Oelke, unpublished paper, are desirable). For example, consider the approach of MacArthur, Recher, and Cody (1966): these researchers compared the difference in bird species diversity which was occasioned by a particular difference in foliage height diversity. Recall that bird species diversity is measured by $- \Sigma_i p_i \log_e p_i$, where p_i is the proportion of all individuals belonging to the ith species; foliage height diversity is similarly measured, except that p_i now becomes the proportion of the foliage that lies in the ith layer. The layers were arbitrarily fixed at 0 to 2 feet, 2 to 25 feet, and over 25 feet (see p. 30). In North America the plot of bird species against foliage height diversity yields a straight line (see Figure 3–8): the points for tropical areas—specifically, Panama and Puerto Rico—however, are widely scattered.

Suppose we assume that the tropical birds are subdividing the habitat more finely. If their subdivision happens to include the degrees of layering of the vegetation, more than three layers would exist. If the same data of Figure 3–7, specifically, the foliage height diversity for Panama, are now based upon four layers—0 to 2 feet, 2 to 10 feet, 10 to 50 feet, and over 50 feet—the scatter disap-

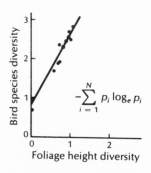

$$-\sum_{i=1}^{N} p_i \log_e p_i$$

FIGURE 3–8. Linear Relationship between MacArthur's Measures of Bird Species Diversity and Foliage Height Diversity. Each point stands for a plot in a different habitat and large enough to hold at least 25 pairs of birds. (Based on MacArthur, MacArthur, and Preer, 1962.)

pears; for Puerto Rico, the scatter attains its minimum by a reduction of the foliage layers to two—0 to 2 feet and over 2 feet.

The forests of Puerto Rico and Panama do not appear to be intrinsically different in amount of layering. The data seem to indicate that Puerto Rican birds show less selectivity in their choice of, or ability to discriminate between, layers than do Panamanian birds. The temperate zone species of North America are intermediate in their degree of "layer selection."

There is also a method for comparing the differences in species diversity for a given degree of difference in foliage diversity which affords a direct test of whether a greater degree of habitat selection occurs in the tropics. According to this method, the foliage height differences between two habitats is given by the FHD of the combined profiles less the average FHD, or

$$\text{FH differential} = -E\left(\frac{P_i + Q_i}{2} \ln \frac{P_i + Q_i}{2}\right)$$
$$+ \tfrac{1}{2}\,(E_i\,P_i/n\,P_i) + (E_i\,Q_i/nqc),$$

(see p. 30 for an explanation of the variables), which issues from 0 (no difference) to a maximum of .693. Figure 3–9 gives their

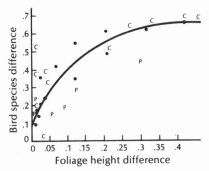

Foliage Height Difference = FHD of combined profiles.

$$\text{Average FHD} = -\sum_i \frac{p_i + q_i}{2} \ln \frac{p_i + q_i}{2} + \frac{1}{2}\left[\sum_i p_i \ln p_i + \sum_i q_i \ln q_i\right]$$

FIGURE 3–9. Illustration of the Relation between the Difference in Foliage Profile and Bird Species Diversity in Pairs of Similar Habitats (C). A two-layered subdivision was used for Puerto Rico, a three-layered one for North America, and a four-layered one for the Canal Zone. The Puerto Rican censuses differ from those of the Canal Zone and North America, suggesting that not only do Puerto Rican birds recognize fewer vertically distributed layers of foliage, but they also show less rigid or stereotyped habitat selection in the horizontal plane. (Based on MacArthur, Recher, and Cody, 1966.)

data, as based upon comparisons of habitats of similar latitude, elevation, and foliage type, with the foliage height diversity index based upon three layers for temperate areas, four for mainland tropics, and two for a tropical island (Puerto Rico). Note that for a given difference in foliage height the temperate regions and

Panama show a similar species difference; Puerto Rico shows less. In other words, if one censuses two habitats in Panama they will differ (in bird species) more from each other than two Puerto Rican habitats differ from each other because different Puerto Rican habitats are more likely to contain similar species than Panamanian or United States habitats.

We must conclude that habitat selection on Puerto Rico is indeed less frequent: the birds of that island *do* have broader habitats. Because their behavior does not differ radically from one habitat to the next, however, one might predict that there are differences in their efficiency in various habitats. The introduction of competitors would probably lead to an increase in habitat selectivity. On the tropical mainlands the bird species diversity per layer of vegetation is not much greater than that of the temperate United States, but since there are more layers recognized by the birds (finer habitat selection), the total diversity of the region is greater.

We can tentatively summarize the answer to our original question as follows: as species diversity increases, so does the degree of habitat selectivity. However, this does not necessarily mean that tropical diversity is high *because* of the narrow or more stereotyped preferences of tropical birds: the one species for which data exist thus far, the banana quit, is clearly capable of broadening its repertoire in the absence of competitors (as on Puerto Rico). Further experimental studies of tropical species are needed to elucidate this point.

Habitat Constancy through Migration

A complication we have ignored thus far is that some animals select seemingly different habitats at different stages of their lives or at different times of the year. Habitat choice in the larval and adult forms of many insects is one example, although another possibility is that the larvae passively remain on whatever substrate they hatch, with selection being exercised only by the adult. Salmon, which live in the ocean for most of their lives, select a freshwater stream—probably the stream of their birth—in which to mate upon attaining reproductive age (see Hasler, 1960). Presumably, both changes in sensory thresholds as well as in central nervous function are the precursors to these changes in habitat, although the question of what motivates the change in preference has yet to be fully answered.

Movements from higher to lower altitudes or latitudes with a consequent change in habitat from feeding to breeding grounds are known for species of virtually every phylum: fish, frogs, snakes, turtles, insects, mammals, and, of course, birds. The latter show by far the most dramatic movement (except, perhaps, for the movements of marine vertebrates), both because of the relatively greater conspicuousness of birds and because a far higher proportion of bird species do in fact move great distances from one habitat to another than is the case for other groups. Thus, although some butterflies such as the monarch fly several thousand miles from summer haunt to winter habitat, most species of lepidoptera are relatively sedentary. Terrestrial vertebrates are generally restricted to movements of a few hundred miles; such short movements, of course, can pose as great a psychological puzzle as longer treks: what triggers the movement, what brings it to a halt, and how is the winter habitat recognized? For a comprehensive survey of the factors involved in migration, however, it is to the birds that we must turn.

Details on the annual stimuli for migration have been summarized elsewhere (see Farner, 1955, and Wolfson, 1959). Although disagreement still exists on the finer points, there is consensus about the general picture: regular daily increases (or decreases) in the duration and time of onset of the photoperiod trigger changes in pituitary activity, which, in turn, influence fat deposition, gonadal development, and motor (migratory) activity. Unfortunately, the physiological details are beyond the scope of this discussion, however intimately they relate to the problem of motivation and perception. Moreover, we shall disregard the question of how migrants find their place of migration. (Recent theories of direction finding and navigation have been critically reviewed by Schmidt-Koenig, 1965). We shall instead focus upon generalities that, hopefully, will provide some clue as to why some species migrate and to the relation between migration and habitat preference.

The extent of the southward movement of species from the

northern hemisphere varies considerably. Some move only to the southern boundary of the temperate zone (about 30° N. latitude); others move well into the tropics; a few such as the golden plover continue south to the temperate regions of the southern hemisphere. About 589 species comprise most of the palearctic avifauna, of which 238 either move within or wholly leave the palearctic region in winter (Moreau, 1952). For a clearer picture of what this means, consider the British Isles, for which about 180 species are recorded as breeding or summer residents. Fifty, or between one fourth and one fifth of these, are migrants that depart before winter. If one considers only the songbirds, which account for about 76 species, almost one third of these species are winter migrants. Very little information is available for migrants that are residents of regions south of the equator. Knowledge of their habits may well cause a revision of some of our generalizations on the significance of migration. A more detailed analysis of North American or nearctic migrants has been made possible by the existence of accurate census data from undisturbed habitats, data that are not available for most other areas. Some of these data are summarized in Figure 3–10, which shows the proportion of migrant *individuals* (not species) to be found among the birds of various virgin or undisturbed habitats. The data are exclusive of waterbirds since waterbirds evidently pose a unique problem.

Even a casual examination of Figure 3–9 reveals a systematic distribution of migrants, even though there is no simple correlation between climate and proportion of migrants. The highest proportion of migrants is found in the deciduous forests of the northeast; in the eastern conifer forests the proportion drops somewhat, dropping still further in the drier coniferous forests of the west; the chaparral, prairies, and deserts have very few migrants indeed. Why might this be?

If we consider an individual bird about to begin its northward flight in the spring, we can imagine that it will persist in this habit (and leave behind its offspring) only if the area to which it goes provides an adequate supply of food, that is, the summer food supplies of migrants must be predictable. Prairies, deserts, and similar dry habitats, in which a summer "bloom" or increase is neither

regular nor inevitable, are not likely to provide predictable supplies, however bountiful the food supplies may be when available.
However, such habitats do provide a reasonably constant supply of
seeds, which are available throughout the year. In short, arid habitats probably neither provide a regularly available summer in-

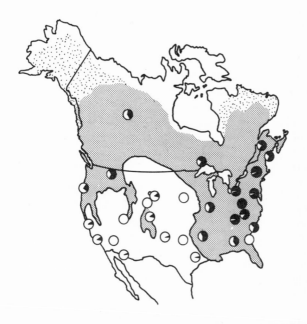

FIGURE 3–10. Proportion of Neotropical Migrant Individuals. The
black sectors of the circles represent the proportion of breeding bird individuals in undisturbed vegetation communities at that locality which
will migrate out of the Nearctic region in the winter. The tinted zone
is roughly the forested region. (Based on MacArthur, 1959.)

crease in food nor show a marked winter decrease. On the other
hand, in coniferous forests the residents can exist year-round, but
no seasonal surplus is regularly available to visitors. And in the
deciduous forest, the burst of spring foliage provides a haven for
hordes of defoliating insects, their parasites, and their predators.
This is a regularly available supply of food and vastly exceeds what

the year-round residents can exploit. The winter conditions, after all, set a limit to the population. Only those birds that do not require foliage to feed upon can persist through a New England winter! Coniferous trees are actually about 40 per cent deciduous, compared with other trees; hence the intermediate proportions of migrants in forests of these trees (MacArthur, 1959).

There is one additional feature of the migratory pattern we shall mention: in northern latitudes of North America, the proportion of migrant individuals exceeds the proportion of migrant species; in the south, this tendency is reversed. In other words, for more northerly areas the average abundance of migrants is greater than that of residents, while in the south the nonmigrant residents are more common. This trend appears to be independent of habitat, but the exact explanation remains obscure.

The character of the breeding grounds, specifically the predictability of the annual production of a surplus food supply, apparently determines whether a seasonal migration may occur. But what is the relation between the breeding habitat and the wintering grounds? It has been calculated that the habitable area (for most birds) of the palearctic region comprises about 13 million square miles (Moreau, 1952). The potential winter quarters of the migrants consist of about 8 million square miles in Africa (exclusive of the Sahara) and another 3 million square miles in Asia; New Guinea, Australasia, and arid Arabia are not included in these figures because these areas are largely unvisited by migrants. Curiously, this is also true for the large island of Madagascar, despite its proximity to the African coast and its ecologically suitable forests. The majority of palearctic species winter in Africa, even though, for many, southeast Asia is far closer, seemingly more accessible, and equally suitable. Within Africa, migrants winter at all latitudes; there is no obvious correlation between latitudinal distribution in the winter quarters and any particular type of habitat. Detailed knowledge of winter habitats is still lacking; however, there do seem to be broad resemblances between the summer and winter homes: European nightingales are found in dense thickets in Africa, as in England; steppes species seek burned-over or barren areas, etc. Similar observations have been made for the warblers of the northeastern United States: in their Central American winter homes they occupy generally similar habitats and appear to behave in a generally similar manner as they do up north. These statements obviously require confirmation (and quantification), but if they are correct, it would appear that migration can effectively reduce the need for behavioral plasticity, for by moving as the seasons change, the migrant maintains itself in a relatively unchanged environment.

At least one other behavioral problem is posed by migration: the effect of winter visitors on the habits of the year-round residents of tropical or southern wintering quarters. Unfortunately, no figures are yet available for the relative numbers of local and migrant birds in any large area. The general impression, however, is that the visitors may often become as numerous as the residents. The very concentration of most of the palearctic migrants from an area of 13 million square miles in an area of less than 8 million square miles would support this impression. What is the effect upon the residents, especially the more aggressively (and continuously) territorial species? If the winter quarters can support so many visitors, why, in the spring and summer, when the migrants are up north, do the residents not pre-empt the space and resources apparently reserved for the visitors' use? There is evidently still much scope for naturalistic studies.

Summary

Particular species of animals are generally associated with a particular kind of habitat. This association may be the result of extrinsic factors such as the selective removal of the more conspicuously colored species by predators or it may be due to the physical structure of the animal which renders it unable to deal with particular habitats, e.g., ducks in the desert. Alternately, the association may be the direct consequence of a psychological preference or choice exercised by the animal.

The development of preferences may be contingent on certain environments which provide more reinforcements than others; they may also depend on imprinting-like processes or on the establishment of socially imposed traditions.

Studies of habitat selection, in addition to their relevance to problems in animal behavior, can also shed light on the causes of the high species diversity of the tropics and the low species diversity of islands. Indeed, it is in studies of habitat selection that psychology and ecology achieve their greatest overlap.

4

TERRITORIALITY

History of the Concept

"IT IS PROPER to this Bird at his first coming to occupy or seize upon one place as its Freehold, into which it will not admit any other Nightingale but its mate." (Nice, 1941.) Thus, did John Ray, writing in 1678, describe the behavior of the European nightingale during its breeding season. Nor was Ray the first to observe and record the occupation of a "Freehold." The generality and essentials of territorial behavior were apparently first formally discussed and recorded by the German ornithologist, Bernard Altum, in the mid-nineteenth century. A translation (Mayr, 1935) of a relevant portion of Altum's *Der Vogel und sein Leben* states:

> [F]or each species of bird, the size of [the] necessary territories is adjusted to its exact ecological requirements and its specific food. While, for example, the Sea-eagle has a territory an hour's walk in diameter, a small wood lot is sufficient for the woodpecker, and a single acre of brush for the Warbler. . . . Birds of different species,

however, can establish their nests close together without the danger of a considerable scarcity of food, because they rarely compete with each other. . . .

An Irishman, C. B. Moffat, elaborated on this theme in 1903 (Nice, 1941):

> My contention . . . was that the battles of male birds, each claiming a territory, resulted in such a parcelling out of the land as must limit the number of breeding pairs . . . and prevent indefinite increase . . . in the course of time, the country—or the parts of it suitable for nidification [nesting]—would come to be completely parcelled out. . . . And once this happy state was arrived at, the number of nesting pairs each year would be exactly the same.

Obviously, the description of animal territories as well as the concept "territoriality" has occupied many authors for many years. Reviews of work done with birds are plentiful; speculations, particularly with regard to primates (including man), are equally abundant. It would be a job of heroic proportions to review all of this literature, and no such enterprise is here contemplated. Let us instead examine selected examples of territorial behavior. A bias toward birds will be evident, but this does not imply a greater significance of territoriality among birds than among other vertebrates. Rather, it reflects the personal predilection of biologists who, for both technical as well as esthetic reasons, have found birds more rewarding to study than other animals. Birds, after all, are relatively easy to observe, to mark and identify individually, they pose little danger, and are a delight to eye and ear. Of how many mammals can this be said? With the recent rush of biologists to Africa (occasioned by the well-founded fear that many species now verge on extinction), the balance will, of course, shift somewhat and we may expect new information on the behavior of primates, cats, deer, antelope, and various carnivores. Papers on territorial behavior in fish, although relatively few in number, also continue to accumulate steadily, as do those on invertebrates. Finally, a literature on the territorial behavior of *Homo sapiens* has sprung into being; some of it, regrettably, is uncritical and sensational to an extreme. We shall return to this point.

The Variety of Territories

Statements concerning "kinds of territories" are subject to two serious errors common to much of ethology: first, if observations are detailed, they may involve arbitrary and biologically meaningless (or fallacious) subdivisions or categorizations of the observed phenomena; insufficient "splitting," on the other hand, may result in an unwieldy mass of data. In the context of studies on communication, Altmann (1965) made this suggestion:

> If one's goal is to draw up an exclusive and exhaustive classification of the animal's repertoire of socially significant behaviour patterns, then these units of behaviour are not arbitrarily chosen. On the contrary, they can be empirically determined. One divides up the continuum of action wherever the animals do. If the resulting recombination units are themselves communicative, that is, if they affect the behaviour of other members of the social group, then they are social messages. Thus, the splitting and lumping one does is, ideally, a reflection of the splitting and lumping that the animals do. In this sense, then, there are natural units of social behavior.

Second, the kind of language in which observations are described may directly influence the hypotheses or conclusions to which they lead. A rat in a maze moves, ultimately, to the chamber in which food has been placed. It has been pointed out (Hinde, 1966) that it makes a considerable difference to the classification or interpretation of this observation if we state that the rat has moved to the "reward box" or if we say that the rat has merely moved to "chamber X." The first implies that the box itself is influencing the probability of the rat's moves being repeated; from "reward" we assume an active influence of the box upon the rat. "Chamber X," however, does not commit us to the view that the box itself is of any importance in the future fashioning of the rat's responses.

Perhaps no other problem in the field of behavior illustrates more clearly the dilemma posed above than does that of animal territories. Classification is an essential prerequisite to analysis of the phenomenon of territoriality, given the unwieldiness and heter-

ogeneity of the concept. Yet, how can we be certain that our classification is neither based upon irrelevant (or misleading) criteria nor
presupposes the explanations for territoriality which we must continue to seek? Consider the following classification by Nice (1941),
one of the most outstanding students of bird territories:

Type A.   Mating, nesting, and feeding ground for young.   This
is to be considered the "classic" example, and is illustrated by a
great many songbirds. For instance, the male North American song
sparrow may stay on or near his territory through most of the winter, but with the coming of spring he will establish "song posts"
around the periphery of the territory—prominent peripheral
perches from which he sings for several minutes, moving fairly regularly from one perch to the next. Thus is his holding of one half to
one acre demarcated. Intruders of the same sex and species will
face a particular "threat" posture display and, for the relatively
rare cases when this does not intimidate them, the intruders will
then be physically driven away. Here is Nice's colorful description:

> The bird in possession of a territory signifies the fact—by his loud
> song, which is repeated from 5 to 7 times a minute from a conspic-
> uous perch. But when a new male appears with intent to settle next
> door, or perhaps to appropriate a portion of the first bird's territory,
> or even to take it entirely, then the owner's behavior changes at once
> and the procedure of territory establishment begins. One of the birds
> sings constantly, 8 to 10 times a minute, usually puffed out and some-
> times vibrating a wing, while the other, silent and menacing, follows
> him closely. After a while the silent bird starts to chase the singer, but
> the latter always returns to the piece of land he covets. Finally, there is
> a fight on the ground, after which the birds separate and each sings
> triumphantly on his own territory, unless, indeed, the new-comer is
> thoroughly beaten and chased away.

Those males that migrate south over the winter will generally
attempt to reoccupy their former territories; if these have already
been occupied, they may either drive out the squatter, move to a
nearby, unoccupied area, or, perhaps, carve out new territories
along the boundaries of other adjoining territories. The territorial
boundaries shift in response to such pressures. Like the females of
most other species, the female song sparrow has no territory of her
own; rather, she adopts that of the mate she selects and aids in the

defense of his territory. She also returns frequently to the same territory, or to one nearby, in successive years.

The nest is built within the territory and most of the food for the young, when they hatch, is collected within its confines. Some of the young males may select their own territories during their first autumn; others, especially those that migrate (some individuals of this species migrate, others do not) may not make a selection until late winter or early spring. During the winter months there is a definite waning in the vigor of the territorial defense; particularly in severe weather the birds may forage over considerable distances and display greater tolerance for one another's presence.

Type B. Mating and nesting, but not feeding, ground. This type of territory differs from the foregoing in that feeding occurs in an area distinct from that where the nests are located. Species with this kind of territory, such as the red-winged and yellow-headed blackbirds of the marshes and the grebes and swans, nest in dense vegetation but feed elsewhere. Obviously, the territories of these birds are much smaller and can be more densely packed together than those of song sparrows.

Type C. Mating station only. The ruff and a number of chicken-like species such as the black grouse and sage grouse form *leks,* or cleared areas where the males gather for communal displays, being visited there by the females. The females bear the entire responsibility for nest construction and rearing of the young and no defense of the nesting area is made, nor is feeding restricted to the nest area. Indeed, since many of the species with this type of territory produce precocial (or down-covered) young, the young wholly abandon the nest soon after hatching.

Type D. Restricted to narrow surroundings of nest. Almost all communally nesting species are included in this category, and of these gulls are perhaps the best-known example. Gull territories are described and illustrated in N. Tinbergen's book, *The Herring Gull's World* (1953).

Type E. Winter territories. This category includes those birds which maintain winter territories in an area geographically distinct from that in which their breeding season territories are held.

Type F. Roosting territories. Finally, some birds such as starlings return at night to a particular resting place where each has a special nook on a building (cited by Nice, 1941). Dairy cattle also show aggressive behavior, and then distress, if they are denied access to their accustomed stalls at milking.

Type G. Collective or communal territories (not included by Nice). These include territories defended by bands of individuals (e.g., Hatch, 1966; Carrick, 1963).

Other classifications of territory types have also been proposed, but, as most of these do not differ fundamentally from the classifications presented above, we need not deal with them here. However, all these classifications share one major disadvantage: some of their rubrics are functional (e.g., *A, B,* and *C,* which reflect the activities of feeding, mating, and nesting), whereas others are descriptive (e.g., *D* and *F,* which depend upon size or site). Such discordances in the character of the classification categories must preclude analysis. Some other basis for classification is required before inquiries into the meaning of territoriality will yield broad generalizations. Finally, this and similar classificatory schemes deal only with territories that are defined as "a defended area." This is surely a succinct definition, but it ignores those intriguing examples which, on other grounds, it seems reasonable to include. For instance, there are cases in which the area being defended is a clearly defined space about the animal that moves with it, rather than being localized in space. Should one exclude the "home range" or area that is used by the animal although not defended? Home ranges are commonly shared by several animals, but this is not invariably so. Clearly, we still lack satisfactory classificatory criteria for territoriality. But at least we can assert their variety!

On the Utility of Territories

The theme developed by the early researchers quoted above is as follows: observations revealed that individual birds, generally males, restricted many of their activities to a specific, clearly delimited area; from this area these birds drove out other males of the same, but generally not of different, species. This defense of an area to which certain activities are restricted is known as "territoriality." The function of territorial behavior, it was assumed, was to assure an adequate food supply. However, the apparent diversity in the kinds of territories—not all territories conformed precisely to the pattern described above—was the source of much further debate. The most authoritative of those who commented was H. Eliot Howard, who has been generally credited with the original formulation of the notion of territorial behavior in his influential *Territory in Bird Life* (1920). In a 1935 letter (cited by Nice, 1941) to E. Mayr, Howard had written:

> My starting point was, and still is, the congenital foundation which is expressed by a male occupying a region and at the same time becoming intolerant of other males within that region. When a Guillemot (or Murre, a seabird that comes ashore only to nest on crowded cliff ledges) occupies a bit of ledge long before an egg is laid and drives away intruders, there is no difference, as far as I can see, in the congenital foundation. From this congenital foundation have grown regions of different size and with different proximate ends, but neither size nor end changes the congenital foundation.

The implication is plain enough: despite the diverstiy in kinds of territories, or the possible diversity in the ends that they serve, territories do possess a common origin, i.e., territorial behavior flows from a single, congenital neural mechanism. This, of course, is an assumption—a reasonable one, perhaps, but not a fact. It is this assumption which underlies many of the quarrels on the definition of "a territory." But let us accept, albeit provisionally, the definition "a defended area to which certain activities are restricted, at least at some seasons," and consider the functions of a territory. The maintenance of a territory provides certain advantages which includes:

1. An increase in the efficiency by which natural resources (e.g., food, refuges, etc.) are utilized as a consequence of activity being restricted to a discrete and familiar area
2. A limitation in the intensity of competition for food (or nest sites), since the number of territories will set a limit on the total breeding density of the population
3. Enhancement of pair formation and pair-bond maintenance because of the existence of a common "home"

4. Reduction of predation both by territorial individuals being spaced and by their enhanced ability to escape when on familiar ground
5. Reduction in time spent in aggression
6. Inhibition of the spread of infectious agents (from Hinde, 1956)

Having compiled a list of the advantages a territorial species might possess over one that is not territorial, we are obliged to ask whether, in fact, there is evidence that supports these suggestions. In dealing with this evidence—and there is little enough—certain facts must be noted:

1. Because a territory does or does not have a certain function in one species does not logically allow an extrapolation to a different species
2. Neither the occurrence of a particular activity, e.g., copulation or feeding, within the territory nor its occurrence without the territory proves anything, in and of itself, about the functions of territories with respect to either mating or feeding. As long as all members of a particular species inhabiting a particular area are either territorial or not, no inferences can be drawn from a catalog of events occurring inside and outside the territory. Indeed, even when some members of the species such as juveniles or some other males are not territorial and do not breed or are seen to feed less well, we cannot conclude that their predicament is due to lack of a territory. These particular individuals might fare no better if they did have territories. The problem is reminiscent of a recent popular controversy: are cigarette smokers more likely to contract cancer, or are those who are susceptible to cancer more likely to smoke? In this instance, evidence involving other sets of correlations is needed.

The belief that territories enhance their occupants' ability to find food efficiently has been widely held by ornithologists. Detailed time-motion analyses ("efficiency studies") of territorial and non-territorial individuals of the same species, sex, and age, made at the same time in similar habitats probably represent the only direct source of evidence: such data are not yet available. However, inferential evidence can be cited: Hinde (1956) lists cases of birds which defend territories around specific food sources; an example is the humming bird, which may abandon a flowery shrub that it had previously defended when the blossoms fall. Thus, when food supply fails, territory is abandoned. Similar inferences may be drawn from the fact that territories (Type *A*) are generally defended against conspecifics, the food requirements of which are identical, but not against other species, which require different foods. However, even in these latter instances it is often true that intruders—whether of a different or even of the same species—are tolerated when they are feeding but are driven out when they begin to sing or display. And there are many cases in which feeding activities regularly occur outside the territory. Thus, we can, at most, assert that for a few species food gathering is promoted by the possession of a territory.

The role of territories in the regulation of population density and the pressures of competition is another matter. If the size of the territory cannot be reduced beyond a certain point, and if successful reproduction requires that the bird possess a territory, the regulatory function of territories becomes a function that is beyond dispute. Can territories not be compressed? In an effort to assay the influence of birds on spruce budworms that were ravaging coniferous northern forests, two researchers (Hensley and Cope, 1951) shot all the singing (i.e., territorial) birds they encountered in a particular area of forest. However, by the following morning the places of the dead tenants had been filled by others. Apparently the woods had been filled with roving individuals, who skulked in the undergrowth and were unable to establish territories until "vacancies" occurred by dint of the researchers' weapons. The implication is that territories cannot be compressed, for otherwise these formerly "homeless" birds would have carved out their own domains prior to the death of the established territorial birds. Additional support for this view is provided by data on habitat selection, summarized by Lack (1966): a particular wood will show an increase in the number of territorial individuals up to a certain point, especially after the addition of artificial nest sites (boxes, in the case of tits); thereafter, new members of the population will find territories in neighboring, ecologically different woods. In years when the number of breeding individuals is relatively low, these latter habitats may not be needed, for they are clearly less preferable. But, as their numbers increase, birds without territories expand into less preferred habitats, rather than reduce the size of their territories within the most favored habitat (e.g., Glass, 1960). This does not imply that territory size is constant, however. Indeed, sizes of territories vary considerably, even within the same area and for members of a single species. Nor is it clear what factors determine the size of a territory. In a study of the availability of food to ovenbirds in relation to territorial size it was found that larger territories had less dense food supplies (Stenger, 1958). And for a species of grouse, the removal of some territorial males caused an increase in the size of their neighbors' territories, or to the occupation of these territories by juvenile birds that would ordinarily not have established territories at all (Watson, 1967). Studies of territories on small islands (Beer et al., 1956) suggest that the wide range in size may be related more to the topography of an area than to the availability of food. Moreover, territorial boundaries may be established along conspicuous discontinuities in the habitat, independently of food resources. In summary, we can say that as long as some lower limit governs size of a territory in a given area, a limit which is periodically manifested, territories can be considered to be incompressible, and thus they can serve to regulate population size.

The importance of controlling population density, by territorial behavior or by other means, is evident because of the devastating effects produced by crowding or high population density. Quite apart from the impetus to predation, disease, or overexploitation of food supplies that high population densities favor, there are a number of other physiological and psychological effects. For example, we know how crowded conditions, particularly among mammals, are associated with adrenal hypertrophy and concomitant increases in reproductive failure, the incidence of psychotic behavior, and mortality (Calhoun, 1962; Christian, 1963; Siegel and Siegel, 1961). Whether territories were *evolved* to regulate density is another matter, which we shall consider shortly.

Does territorial behavior enhance pair-bond formation and

maintenance? Certainly the existence of a fixed rendezvous must aid two individuals to find one another after a separation. The most relevant observations bearing on this point are those which indicate that in some species territorial behavior persists only until pair-formation is complete. An opposing observation, that other species form pairs without exhibiting territorial behavior, can remind us of the dangers of generalizing.

The role of territories in reducing predation is another controversial matter. *A priori,* it is reasonable to believe that being familiar with a small area of terrain would increase a bird's chances of making a successful escape when threatened. However, if a predator is also territorial, this advantage could be nullified. Territorial behavior can also limit the density of breeding aggregations, reducing the effects of predation through dispersion, although the species that are bothered by few nest predators may still be territorial, and those which are bothered by many may not. Little can be deduced from such observations except that there is an apparent multiplicity of functions of different species' territories. With regard to other presumed functions of territories, little can be said.

Finally, it must be mentioned that interspecific territorial strife may also occur. This has been documented for indigo and lazuli buntings, titmice and chestnut-backed chickadees, and red-winged and yellow-headed blackbirds (as cited by Orians, 1961). Orians describes the interactions that occur in the cattail marshes where two kinds of blackbirds which are quite different in appearance breed:

> Most marshes on the refuge support breeding populations of both species of Blackbirds and in all cases there is interspecific territoriality. Redwing territories are established by late March and typically encompass all available emergent vegetation. The Redwings are evicted from portions of the marshes, usually those with deeper water and more sparse vegetation, by the incoming Yellowheads in mid- and late April. During this period interspecific aggression is common though usually not of the intensity characteristic of intraspecific encounters . . . with infrequent exceptions, none of the usual territorial displays are used in interspecific encounters. . . . Yellowheads are dominant over Redwings when the two species meet at feeding

grounds off the breeding territories. . . . Yet, in territorial interactions, dominance is related to the nature of the vegetation, since Redwings are dominant over Yellowheads on the peripheries of most marshes.

In general, as Orians notes, interspecific territoriality involves species that breed in structurally simple habitats, marshes, grasslands, and tundra, where the foliage height diversity is low. Presumably, it also reduces the available means for exploiting food resources. Thus, interspecific territoriality should be common in such simple habitats and should involve species that have only recently begun living near each other. Also, individuals that have not been able to find space in the optimal habitat preferred by their kind, a habitat sufficiently complex to discourage all interspecific strife, may be forced to settle in less suitable, simpler peripheral areas, where interspecific territoriality cannot be avoided. Given enough time and a stable environment, interspecific conflicts ought to diminish. Orians' deductions are supported by work done on several small islands off the coast of Mexico (Grant, 1966). Moreover, other researchers have found that the small size of these islands has the same ecological effect as a reduction in habitat diversity or complexity (MacArthur and Wilson, 1963). Interspecific territoriality does not exist on these islands because, presumably, one member of every competing pair of species has been eliminated, for these islands show many fewer pairs of similar coexisting species than do ecologically similar areas of the mainland.

The Evolution of Territoriality

Certainly the one sound generalization possible about avian territories is that they are diverse: they vary with regard to type (solitary, communal, or pair), size, temporal stability, and function, to list only the major parameters. Although there have been few analyses of mammalian territoriality, those few studies have encouraged extrapolations from birds to primates (see, for example, Carpenter, 1958; Schaller, 1963; Goodall, 1965, to list but a handful of the primate studies). One of the logical consequences of the notion of diversity of territories, however, is that it weakens the assumption that a single selective pressure is a prelude to territorial behavior: it is possible that on many occasions territoriality evolved independently in response to different pressures.

An alternate view to that of "diverse origins," which has been proposed by J. L. Brown (1964), reconciles the apparently diverse types of territorial behavior within a single theory. According to Brown, territoriality is most accurately regarded as site-dependent aggressiveness. Aggressive behavior itself is likely to be favored by natural selection when its employment enhances survival or survival of offspring. The aggressive behavior could be linked with defense of food, mates, mating places, nests, or any other requisites for survival or reproductive success. Whether aggression actually is employed to defend any or all of these resources depends upon the "dependability" of these resources, that is, their availability and accessibility to each individual, and the cost (in time and energy) of obtaining and defending them.

> Too much aggression in the absence of a short supply of the disputed requisite would eventually be detrimental. Consequently, a balance must be achieved between the positive values of acquired food, mate, nesting area, protection of family, etc., and the negative values of loss of time, energy, and opportunities, and risk of injury. Where this balance may lie in any particular species is influenced by a great variety of factors. . . .
> Within the population those individuals with the optimal balance of the genetic factors working for and against a particular form of aggressiveness . . . would [become] the norms for the population. [*Ibid.*]

The character of the territory that evolves—if any kind of territoriality does evolve—thus depends upon the economics of site-dependent aggression. Marine birds, which nest colonially, feed from the sea: for these birds defense of feeding areas is impractical if not impossible, but defense of a small area to be used for mating and nesting is indeed possible. Sage grouse, however, range widely in their search for food; for these birds the major cause of mortality appears to be predation during the juvenile stage. Thus there seems to be only a limited value in defending a feeding area; the major problem for the sage grouse is to remain inconspicuous while the chicks are still maturing, and this interest is better served without territorial defense.

Brown also calls attention to the often slighted vast differences in the character and extent of territorial behavior exhibited by closely related species. His work on the scrub jay and Mexican jay (Brown, 1963) is a case in point. The former bird is aggressively territorial, and the latter, although it inhabits ecologically similar regions, maintains only weakly defended communal territories. A comparable situation exists for the red-winged and tri-colored blackbirds of the west coast (Orians, 1961). The existence of differences of such magnitude in what must be recently differentiated species suggests that territorial behavior is a labile trait, very responsive to shifts in selective pressures and easily changed or even lost altogether. This last point is perhaps best illustrated by considering all kinds of avian social organization, not just territoriality. In the nonbreeding season, the social behavior and organization of birds may be characterized as "relatively solitary" or "gregarious." In the former case individuals may be so widely dispersed that territorial boundaries are not apparent. However, territorial boundaries may also be contiguous, as for the English robin which we described previously. Nonbreeding individual English robins are gregarious and they may form constantly shifting flocks that either utilize fixed loci for roosting or feeding or wander about as dictated by expediency. One more possibility is the formation of flocks of constant composition which either defend collective territories (e.g., the Galapagos mockingbirds, Hatch, 1966) or follow particular paths (e.g., winter juncos, Sabine, 1955). Four major categories of social organization can be recognized during the breeding season: wide dispersion, colonial aggregation, communal organizations, and communal display grounds or arenas (e.g., the "leks" or communal display grounds of the grouse). (Crook, 1965.)

The foregoing briefly characterizes the different forms the social organization of birds may take. Now let us ask: which ecological parameters can be expected to influence social structures? Three main groups of parameters are the most important: (1) the general character of the food required, i.e., does the bird require infrequent large feedings, as hawks do, or does the bird require more frequent feedings, as with tits which may require an insect every 2½ seconds throughout a winter day; (2) the degree of dispersion of the food supply; and (3) the character and availability of nest sites. While it has been possible heretofore to treat this question only speculatively, convincing evidence exists of the close relationship between the ecological forces that control animal populations and the character of their social systems, of which territoriality is but one type. (Crook, 1965.)

Summary

The concept of territoriality was already explicit in the seventeenth century, in the writings of John Ray, although the widespread nature and significance of territorial behavior was not formally recognized until two centuries later. Bernard Altum was the ornithologist to whom credit for these early discussions belongs, although Eliot Howard is generally given credit because of his influential book, *Territory in Bird Life* (1920).

The basic notion of a territory is that it is an area that is defended against intruders of the same species and sex. However, there also exist many instances of defense against members of alien species, or corporate defense of communal territories. Similarly, there is a great variety of purposes served by territories from the provision of an exclusive food supply, to offering exclusive mating or nesting opportunities. It is apparent that territorial behavior represents a set of adaptations that differs from species to species.

5

ADAPTATION

On Adaptation

. . . [A] hen which has just paired up with a cock in early spring is at first unaware of the boundaries of her mate's territory. She wanders in all directions, and whenever she trespasses is promptly threatened by the neighbouring owner. Hens soon come to recognize places where they are attacked. Thus one hen was vigorously driven from a tree which happened to be just inside the neighbour's boundary. Twice in the next ten minutes she again began to fly towards the same tree, but then sheered off in mid-air as if recollecting her former reception.

D. Lack, *The Life of the Robin* (1943)

THUS DOES A female robin come to share in the defense of a discrete plot of land, her territory. And this phenomenon was observed and remarked upon long before birdwatchers aspired to the status of "scientist." At least one of the reasons for the interest in territorial behavior shown by students of natural history lies in the examples it affords of "adaptation," although the kind of adaptation it represented was another matter. Territoriality has been variously looked upon as an adaptation for conserving or sharing food, reducing predation, enhancing parental-filial relations or favoring mate constancy, and eliminating or controlling aggression, to mention but a few of its alleged functions. Yet all students of animal territories agree that these territories are adaptive. We might well first inquire: What is an "adaptation"? Indeed, it is a concept that has become so pervasive, important, and ill-defined in biological (including much psychological) literature as to merit the establishment of a specific discipline devoted to its study. *Teleonomy* is the term that one author has recently proposed for this discipline, and he has himself written a provocative introduction to the subject (G. C. Williams, 1966). But obviously the notion of adaptation antedates Williams' treatment. Aristotle, in his distinction between "final" and "efficient" causes, can probably claim priority for the idea, but the modern development of the concept as used by biologists owes much to the insights of Lotka (1956) and Gause (1942), who emphasize that "adaptation" implies conformity. For instance, when a bear's fur matches the color of its background, the bear is said to be "adapted" to or in conformation with that background. However, the measure of the degree of adaptation is relative to other individuals and to other situations. Can a quantitative statement of the degree of adaptation ever be provided? Consider the following example, provided by Lotka: let the degree of conformity be represented by the distance between a point A and a fixed point O. We will let any position nearer O than A represent an adaptation superior to that represented by the distance AO. Suppose that O is the center of a sphere and AO its radius; then, the position that must be occupied by an improved adaptation would lie within the sphere, i.e., if A is shifted the distance r, its translation will represent improved adaptation only if it is brought closer to the sphere's center O. If r is very small, the chance for an improved adaptation will tend toward its limit of ½. The chance for improvement decreases as r increases $2AO$, or d, the diameter. In short, the probability of an improved adaptation equals $½ \left(1 - \dfrac{N}{D} \right)$, at least for a three-dimensional model. The relative degree of adaptation may be taken as the ratios of any particular AO to its theoretic minimum or of the AO's of two different individuals.

In considering the nature of "adaptation" it is important to distinguish adaptation from "adaptability." If the former represents a measure of an initial state of conformation, or susceptibility, the latter is the capacity for undergoing modification. The white polar bear's pelage or coloring may conform to the color of his background, but it cannot change color. The polar bear's color, then, represents an adaptation, rather than adaptability, but the chameleon's capacity for change shows adaptability. We stress this distinction because the capacity to respond by adaptation or adaptability may well be inversely proportional. The experimental evidence comes largely from Gause, who found he could acclimatize *clones,* or inbred lines, of protozoans to high concentrations of salt or to extreme temperature. Future generations of this organism were "adapted" to the newer, more extreme conditions. However, they were then no longer able to tolerate rapid, although moderate, shifts in temperatures or salinity. Nonacclimatized strains were not able to tolerate the extreme conditions of their acclimatized siblings but could tolerate more rapid, if less extreme, changes in condition. They were adaptable, if not adapted! Parallel considerations underlie many arguments about the "advantages" of learning versus instinct, phenotypic change versus genotypic change (e.g., Bateson, 1966), or flexibility versus speed for computers. We cannot forget that the concept "adaptation" is, in its broadest sense, many-faceted.

When we examine some particular process or mechanism, the appropriate question to ask is: "What is its function?" Actually, we are asking what is the immediate or proximate end that is served. The correct answer may not be obvious at first. The immediate function of the slit pupil in nocturnal animals may, in fact, be apparent (it allows for a greater range in pupil size, hence light-gathering ability, than does a round pupil), but that of dark skin or the A-B-O blood-groups is less so; and the function of the reptilian pineal gland is still essentially unknown (the many hypotheses concerning its function notwithstanding). But, even when an immediate end or effect can be specified and demonstrated, does this mean we have proven the process or structure to be "an adaptation" for that end? Consider the following illustrations (taken, for the most part from Williams, 1966):

1. A fox on his first visit to a henhouse after a heavy snowfall has difficulty fording the drifts. As he walks, however, his paws sift and pack snow, forming a path along which he can more speedily and efficiently retrace his steps upon seizing his prey. Can we properly claim the paws are an adaptation for trail blazing?
2. A flying fish leaps abruptly into the air, glides, and then returns smoothly to the water. Are its extended pectoral fins, which permits the glide, an adaptation for returning the fish to the water?
3. Earthworms move considerable quantities of soil through their guts, thereby loosening and aerating the soil. Good gardeners value this feature of earthworm behavior. Is soil ingestion an adaptation to enhance the quality of soil?
4. The white pelage of polar bears effectively camouflages them from the eyes of their prey. Is this an adaptation?
5. Many social insects have a worker caste of reproductively inert or sterile individuals. Is this individually disadvantageous trait an adaption by the group?

The characteristics and adaptations of individuals are shaped by natural selection. By this we mean that those individuals whose contributions to the gene pool of the future are proportionately greatest will impart their characteristics to future generations. The measure of this proportionate contribution is known as *fitness*. Adaptations are considered to be traits that increase fitness. They need not be essential for the survival of the individual, but they must be advantageous to survival. And some of these characteristics, called *pleiotropic* characteristics, may resemble the inevitable or accidental by-products of other features; even when these characteristics are useful, however, they should not be considered adaptations. Thus, in analyzing the above list, we can say that it is unnecessary and incorrect to regard the fox's paws as a specific adaptation for packing snow, although the paws will eventually serve this purpose. We must realize that the paws would have evolved even in the absence of snow. Similarly, the flying fish will return to the water whether it has pectoral fins or not. Only if a *smooth* return, as aided by the fins, can be shown to increase fitness, can the fins be considered adapted to this end. The earthworm's worthwhile gardening activities, considered from the farmer's point of view, cannot, for the earthworm, be shown to have significance beyond its nutritional needs. However, the white pelage of polar bears, as well as that of many arctic animals, can be shown to increase fitness: many experiments (Sumner, 1935; also, see Cott, 1940, for his list of references) have documented the value of concealing coloration. But this does not suggest that this adaptation is essential to survival. If all polar bears were pink, no one bear would be at a disadvantage relative to the others. They might exert more effort to find food (since they would not be well camouflaged), which might lead to a reduced population density, i.e., more prey organisms per bear, but it would not *necessarily* endanger their survival. In short, adaptations are traits that increase fitness and which evolve for this reason rather than because of an unavoidable link with some other trait.

The question of group adaptations, finally, presents a particularly knotty problem, if only because the notion of "group adaptation" is thoroughly woven into our folklore. By group adaptation it is meant that individual interests are compromised to those of the group to allow for the emergence of characteristics beneficial to the group, although inimical to the individual. The sterile worker castes of social insects are one example: sterility certainly would seem to confer a limited fitness upon an individual, however useful to his group a sterile caste might be. We may refer to such subordination of individual benefits for the welfare of a group as *altruism,* and we will deal with this phenomenon at greater length below.

Altruism and Group Selection

The lioness's fight unto death to protect her cubs evokes our sympathy; so does the injured-wing ruse by which many birds decoy an intruder from their nest. The seemingly meek acceptance of death by drones once the queen bee has been fertilized may seem less laudable, but all these phenomena are recognized as instances of altruism.

Two forms of altruistic behavior can be readily understood without reference to any novel form of natural selection: First, in highly social species such as man, the (occasionally unreciprocated) helpfulness of strangers toward one another may stem from nothing more profound than the fact that an individual who makes as much as possible of his friendships and keeps his antagonisms to a minimum will be more fit. Nor does every such altruist have to be more fit as a consequence of his concern (conscious or otherwise) for others, so long as, in the long run, *most* altruists are more fit. Their greater fitness will presumably derive from the fact that, in times of need, they, or their offspring, are more likely to obtain succor from others than are more self-seeking individuals. The second form of easily explicable altruism is that which is directed primarily toward members of one's own family. Each offspring carries half the genes of each parent. Thus, if a parent sacrifices himself for the sake of his children, his genes will not be lost and his fitness will not necessarily be reduced. The degree of altruism that selection favors is directly proportional to the closeness of the genetic relationship of the individuals involved. Specifically, if the gain to a relative of degree r is K times the disadvantage to the altruist, selection will favor the altruistic "genes" if K is greater than $1/r$ (Hamilton, 1964). This would appear to provide an explanation for the otherwise peculiar reproductive "adaptations" of the social insects, i.e., the sterile castes. However, a third form of group adaptation or "altruism" which has also been postulated and advanced as an explanation for a host of ecological problems (Wynne-Edwards, 1962) is less easily explained: the notion that behavior which benefits a group confers a "fitness" upon the group that is relatively independent of the consequences to the individual who is doing the behaving. For example, suppose that one group of deer had no socially organized communication system, while another was so organized that whenever one animal saw a predator he would similtaneously warn his fellows and they would then scatter. By virtue of the simultaneity of his fellows' flight, the sentinel would then be in greater danger than if he had been the first to flee, leaving the others unalerted until his escape had been completed. Yet groups without such social warning systems are uncommon, so we assume that the net advantages of group action outweigh all its disadvantages to any particular individual. Deer that are members of socially organized herds thus have a greater average fitness than those without such organization.

Superficially, this is a plausible argument, and those of us who want to find a biological basis for an altruistic ethic are particularly pleased to have such arguments available. (As a young pacifist this author frequently cited similar arguments [Kropotkin, 1914; Allee, 1938] in support of political doctrines. Later, embarrassed by the naiveté [irrelevance?] of these citations, I was glad to find what at first appeared to be more substantial support, in a treatise by Wynne-Edwards [1962]. Alas!) If those who seek support for political or ethical systems in biology undertake critical examination of the arguments for the existence of group adaptations and group selection, they find them lacking on two counts: first, the data cited to support their claims are inadequate, i.e., those cases cited in evidence are explicable in ways that require no more, and often less, in the way of intravening assumptions. Second, the notion of group selection presupposes the existence of genetic or evolutionary mechanisms that seem highly unlikely, if not impossible, to exist. These two points deserve a detailed scrutiny (see also Wiens, 1966, for a detailed critique of group selection). First, recall that organisms do not reproduce in an errorless fashion. However, mutants—the organisms resulting from genetic "errors" in reproduction—are generally less fit than their forebears for the same reason that random tampering with a good quality watch is less likely to improve than impair its function (see p. 93). Not only very occasionally do random changes in genotype lead to increased fitness in the original environment; also environments change and thus some mutants survive. This is how organisms evolve and the constitution of populations change. It is difficult to understand how one can speak of communities or groups evolving except insofar as their constituent individuals evolve, for groups lack a hereditary base, except in a metaphorical sense. Groups can only *change*. As Lack points out:

organisms evolve . . . but one should not speak of communities doing so, and the distinction between "change" and "evolve" is much more than purely verbal, because the use of the term "evolution" in relation to communities brings with it implicit concepts which are strictly relevant only to organisms and their hereditary differences.

Therefore, the major questions one must ask are: how can group selection (assuming it exists) overcome the effects of natural selection (which operates only upon individuals)? and, second, cannot the observations which cause group selection to be offered as an explanation be more readily handled in other ways? We can deal with these questions the most easily by referring to a particular set of observations. Since the leading proponents of group selection have considered the regulation of population density to be one of the outstanding effects of group selection, we, too, shall consider one particular aspect of this problem—namely, what limits the clutch size of songbirds? At this point, however, we shall make a brief digression to provide some insight into the implications and relevance of this question.

Group Selection and a Digression on the Regulation of Animal Numbers

Animal numbers are relatively constant. Although they may fluctuate from year to year, particularly where the environment has undergone changes, the fluctuations are transitory and, over longer periods, trivial. Three theories of population control have been proposed to account for this relative constancy. (These are discussed in some detail by Lack, 1966, whose book also provides a detailed bibliography.) The first theory, often associated with the name of A. J. Nicholson, proposes that population growth is density-dependent, i.e., the rate of growth is inversely proportional to the numbers of animals. The mechanisms whereby this regulation by negative feedback is managed may vary; (1) as numbers increase, their food supply may diminish, increasing mortality or decreasing fecundity; (2) high densities can attract predators which then become more efficient harvesters of their prey; and (3) the crowding resulting from an increase in numbers may cause physiological changes such as changes in adrenal activity, with a resultant decrease in fecundity and viability. (Particular examples will be found in Lack, 1966; Christian, 1963; Slobodkin, 1961.) The theory that population growth is density-dependent includes no assumptions as to which, if any, of these regulative mechanisms is operative. To restate the theory more precisely,

$$\frac{\triangle N}{\triangle t} = K(K - N),$$

where K is a constant representing the maximum density possible at any given moment, and N the number present at a given point in time (t).

Another view (advanced by Andrewartha and Birch, 1954) attributes the relative constancy of numbers (over many years) to periodic natural catastrophes such as sudden freezes or droughts which decimate populations and prevent them from increasing to excess population levels. However, even the strongest supporters of this point of view admit that for some animals population growth is density-dependent since environmental events do not always restrict growth to the rates they actually obtain. Opponents have claimed that even populations subjected to extreme environmental pressures are still subject to density-dependent growth.

A third point of view, recently popularized by Wynne-Edwards (1962), recognizes that food supplies are the ultimate arbiter of population density and that the rate of growth diminishes with population size. However, this theory then proposes that organisms have evolved a "code" (in the form of social or epideictic displays) that (1) provides each individual with information on the size of the population, and (2) affects his behavior in an appropriate fashion so as to anticipate, and thus avoid, food shortage. Suppose it is personally disadvantageous for a given individual to restrict his reproductive activities. However, if by so doing he provides the population of which he is a member an advantage, might not "group selection" promote his self-denial?

Where [group selection and individual selection] conflict, as they do when the short-term advantage of the individual undermines the future safety of the race, group selection is bound to win, because the race will suffer and decline, and be supplanted by another in which anti-social advancement of the individual is more rigidly inhibited. [*Ibid.*, p. 20.]

The above contains a logical error—that if a given act by an organism is truly disadvantageous to it, i.e., if such an act reduces the organism's own "fitness" (as previously defined), the genes the animal carries must disappear no matter how much its actions benefit the "group." On the other hand, if the animal's actions increase its own fitness, it is irrelevant whether or not they also aid the group; any advantage gained by the group is then fully explained by the action of natural selection and nothing else need be involved.

Consider the case of the European swift: its clutch varies from one to four eggs and since clutch size is apparently a heritable trait, one might expect that swifts that produce large clutches would gradually replace swifts that produce smaller clutches. Indeed, one might even expect a five- or six-egg-producing swift to evolve. Examination of "survivorship" within clutches of different sizes, however, reveals that more fecund females do not, in fact, make the larger contributions to the gene pool. For example, in 1961, at Oxford, Lack (1966) demonstrated that the average number of young that survived to the fledgling stage in two-egg clutches was 1.9, in three-egg clutches, 2.3, and in four-egg clutches, only 1.4. Thus, the females who produced only two eggs were actually more fit (i.e., they left more young) than those that produced four eggs! The obvious point is that a regulation or restriction of reproductive proclivities is just as likely to increase the fitness of the individual concerned as to benefit the group to which he belongs. Crowded deer reduce their reproductive activity, but a doe which remains barren one season may actually increase her own chances of leaving offspring another season: her response to crowding (inhibition of reproduction) can be explained by the action of natural selection, and requires no contrary principle. Group selection and group adaptations, in short, are unnecessary concepts that neither provide explanations nor lead to new insights. The origin and maintenance of altruism can be accounted for by the same explanations that apply to other types of individual adaptations. And these explanations must be applicable to the phenomenon of territoriality as well.

Extrapolations to Man

If we reject the notions of Brown or Crook about the evolution of territoriality, we can make few *a priori* pronouncements about the territorial behavior of animals that have not yet been studied; the limit to our extrapolation would be a prediction that there is a diversity of territorial types at all phyletic levels. However, even if we do accept Brown's and Crook's views (which show great promise), we can still make no assertions about the character (i.e., the type and function) of territorial behavior for any particular animal. The utility of the models Brown and Crook have presented lies in their ordering of observed phenomena rather than in their predictive power. And the apparent lability of territorial behavior is an important consideration.

The author emphasizes these facts because of occasional popular attempts to derive conclusions about human "territorial" behavior from studies of nonhuman animals (e.g., Ardrey, 1966). These vulgar (because so commercially successful?) accounts rest on abysmal ignorance of the diversity of territoriality in general and of the implications of this diversity, even when it is treated in a simple explanatory scheme such as Brown's. In short, there are neither factual nor theoretical bases for assertions regarding the role of ancestral territorial "impulses" in the structuring (or fracturing) of human social behavior. The anthropologist Edmund Leach has detailed and documented this point in an important article (1966) in which he summarizes the popular view we are criticizing as follows:

> Ethologists have shown that the phenomenon of territoriality recurs throughout the animal kingdom. Individual members of a particular species identify with a particular territory. All other members of the same species are dichotomized as friends and strangers. Strangers are attacked if they intrude in *our* territory; the deeper the intrusion the more violent the counter-aggression.

Thereupon, as Leach points out, the uncritical writer may make two errors. First, he may assume that territorial behavior occurs in all animals and must therefore occur in man. However, it should now be apparent how un-universal territoriality really is, particularly among the nonhuman primates (e.g., compare Schaller's firsthand description of the gentle mountain gorilla [1963] with the imagined aggressiveness of Ardrey's [1966] mythical hominids). The second error the uncritical writer may make is confusing a motor response—overt behavior—with its underlying mechanism and motivation. To quote Leach again,

> If we define the word "aggression" in a behavioristic (i.e., objective) way, . . . then man, like any other animal, has built-in "innate" ways of exhibiting aggression. What is in dispute is whether man likewise has a built-in tendency to defend his home territory so that the precise circumstances in which he will exhibit this "aggressive behavior" are predictable.

No evidence has been advanced that favors this claim, but various field studies of nonhuman primates all suggest (although they certainly do not prove) a far different conclusion.

Does it follow from the foregoing disclaimer that the facts and theories of animal behavior have no bearing on man? Obviously not. But do we disclaim extrapolations that explain uniquely human social and ethical behavior? Again, no. An instructive example of a reasonable extrapolation is to be found in Waddington's (1960) treatment of the evolution of ethics, although whether his notions are correct is another matter. They are cited below to indicate that the rejection of territoriality as relevant to man's behavior is not based on any general prejudice against biological explanations of social and ethical systems.

Waddington points out that a *sine qua non* for sociocultural transmission of information is a recipient—specifically, a responsive recipient. The evolution of a distinctive human animal involves the inheritance of traditions as well as genes, traditions which can be transmitted only if the youngest generation is responsive to the teachings of older generations. From the beginning, therefore, given the advantages of a cultural inheritance, selection must have favored those animals that accepted the social teachings and structures of their elders. The newborn human infant must, from the beginning, accept authority.

Ethical beliefs are merely strongly held beliefs that allow the individual to distinguish between "right" and "wrong" as determined by his society. The reality of the notions of "right" and "wrong" is evidenced by the existence of "conscience" or feelings of propriety or guilt even in young children. Once established, ethical beliefs are not impervious to change; they can later be re-examined, altered, or perhaps altogether rejected. The point made by Waddington is that given the power of selection for the social transmission of information, it was inevitable that man should evolve as an ethical animal. This says nothing about the content of the ethical system. However, this, too, could, within very broad limits, be dictated by natural selection. Thus, the advocates of beliefs and acts that lead to reduced fitness (e.g., intensive inbreeding or incest) would find themselves (and their views) replaced. Conversely, we previously described how the tendency to perform altruistic acts could evolve.

One of the principal points open to debate in Waddington's thesis is his portrayal of the human infant as an authority acceptor. Fortunately, this issue is open to experiment. Waddington cites the studies of Piaget and Anna Freud and finds within them considerable conformation for authority-acceptance as a primary factor in the development of the child. Animal studies of imprinting (reviewed by Sluckin, 1965, and Bateson, 1966) also provide relevant suggestions, although conclusive evidence on this question of early learning and belief-formation still has not been found. However, comparative studies of animal behavior and evolution do shed light on the origins of human behavior, even ethical behavior, although this presupposes the ability to critically and discriminatingly distinguish analogies from homologies.

Summary

Adaptations, including those adaptations that fall under the rubric of territoriality, are actually measures of conformity. To what extent are such measures appropriately applied to groups rather than to individuals? Some authors have argued for the existence of group adaptations which arise through group selection, a view which implies the development of traits harmful to the individual but advantageous to the group. Altruistic behavior and behavioral mechanisms that regulate population growth are often cited as examples. However, it is relatively simple to show that both these and similar kinds of behavior can, in fact, develop as a consequence of natural selection. The concept of group selection need not provide us with an explanation, which is fortunate in view of the illogical and contradictory nature of this concept. With respect to altruism, for instance, if the gain to a relative of degree r is K times the disadvantage to the altruist, the altruistic trait will evolve only if K exceeds $1/r$. Population control mechanisms can also be understood without recourse to vague concepts such as group selection.

As for territoriality, it probably represents not a single adaptation but a host of different adaptations serving different purposes for various animals. This fact alone precludes a facile extrapolation to man and a biological justification of property rights. This does not mean that human behavior—even in the moral realm—is unrelated to biological phenomena. For example, adequate learning ability for infants, clearly a trait that natural selection has fostered, requires a brain that accepts authority, and this leads to the appearance of behavioral or psychological constraints of the type we call ethics. Even the contents of ethical systems, along with their very existence, may be influenced by natural selection; the loss of fitness that results from extensive inbreeding could underlie the near-universality of incest taboos. We can thus say that uniquely human behavior does not lack a biological base, but that direct extrapolations from birds to mammals or from birds to men are likely to be foolish unless they account for all relevant evolutionary and ecological factors.

REFERENCES

Allee, W. C. 1938. Cooperation among Animals. H. Schuman, N.Y.

Altmann, S. A. 1965. Sociobiology of rhesus monkeys. II. Stochastics of social communication. J. Theoret. Biol. 8:490–522.

Andrewartha, H. G., and L. C. Birch. 1954. The Distribution and Abundance of Animals. University of Chicago Press, Chicago, Ill.

Ardrey, R. 1966. The Territorial Imperative: a personal inquiry into the animal origin of property and nation. Atheneum, N.Y.

Bateson, G. 1963. The role of somatic change in evolution. Evolution 17:529–539.

Bateson, P. G. 1966. The characteristics and context of imprinting. Biolog. Revs. 41:177–220.

Beer, J., L. Frengel, and N. Hansen. 1956. Minimum space requirements of some nesting passerines. Wilson Bull. 68:200–209.

Bergman, G. 1955. Die Beziehung zwischen Bodenfarbe der Reviere und Farbe des Kuecken bei *Hydroprogne t.* und *Sterna m.* Ornis Fennica 32:69–81.

Bowman, R. I. 1961. Morphological differentiation and adaptation in the Galapagos finches. Univ. Calif. Pub. Zool. 58:1–326.

Brown, J. L. 1963. Social organization and behavior of the Mexican jay. Condor 65:126–153.

Brown, J. L. 1964. The evolution of diversity in avian territorial systems. Wilson Bull. 76:160–169.

Brown, J. L. 1966. Types of group selection. Nature 211:870.

Brown, W. L., and E. O. Wilson. 1956. Character displacement. Systemat. Zool. 5:49–65.

Burghardt, G. M. 1967. Chemical-cue preferences of inexperienced snakes: comparative aspects. Science 157:718–721.

Cain, A. J., and P. M. Sheppard. 1954. Natural selection in Cepaea. Genetics 39:89–116.

Calhoun, J. B. 1962. A "behavioral sink." *In* E. L. Bliss (ed.), Roots of Behavior. Harper and Brothers, N.Y., p. 295–315.

Carpenter, C. R. 1958. Territoriality: a review of concepts and problems. *In* A. Roe and G. Simpson (eds.), Behavior and Evolution. Yale University Press, New Haven, Conn., p. 224–250.

Carrick, R. 1963. Ecological significance of territory in the Australian magpie (Gymnorhina tibicen). Proc. XIII Internat. Ornith. Congr., p. 740–753.

Christian, J. J. 1963. Endocrine adaptive mechanisms and the physiologic regulation of population growth. *In* W. V. Mayer and R. G. van Gelder (eds.), Physiological Mammalogy. Academic Press, N.Y., p. 189–353.

Connell, J. H., and E. Orias. 1964. The ecological regulation of species diversity. Amer. Natur. 99:399–414.

Cott, H. B. 1940. Adaptive Coloration in Animals. Oxford University Press, N.Y.

Crook, J. H. 1965. The adaptive significance of avian social organizations. Sympos. Zoolog. Soc. London 14:181–218.

Crowell, K. 1961. The effects of reduced competition in birds. Nat. Acad. Sci. 47:240–243.

Dammermann, K. W. 1948. The fauna of Krakatua: 1883–1933. Verhandlungen K. Akademie Math (Nat.) 44:1–594.

Emlen, J. 1956. A method for describing and comparing avian habitats. Ibis 98:555–576.

Erickson, R. P. 1963. Sensory neural patterns and gustation. *In* Proc. Internat. Sympos. Olfaction and Taste. I. Pergamon Press, N.Y., p. 205–213.

Farner, D. S. 1955. The annual stimulus for migration: experimental and physiologic aspects. *In* A. Wolfson (ed.), Recent Studies in Avian Biology. University of Illinois Press, Urbana, Ill., p. 198–237.

Fisher, J., and R. A. Hinde. 1950. The opening of milk bottles by birds. Brit. Birds 42:347–357.

Fisher, R. A. 1958. The Genetical Theory of Natural Selection. 2nd rev. Dover, N.Y.

Flint, R. F. 1957. Glacial and Pleistocene Geology. John Wiley and Sons, N.Y.

Gause, G. J. 1934. The Struggle for Existence. Williams and Wilkins, Baltimore, Md.

Gause, G. J. 1942. The relation of adaptability to adaptation. Quart. Rev. Biol. 17:99–114.

Glass,. P. 1960. Factors governing density in the chaffinch in different types of wood. Arch. Neerl. Zool. 13:466–472.

Goldschmidt, R. 1955. Theoretical Genetics. University of California Press, Berkeley, Calif.

Goodall, J. 1965. Chimpanzees of the Gombe Stream Preserve. *In* I. de Vore (ed.), Primate Behavior. Holt, Rinehart and Winston, N.Y.

Goode, J. P. 1950. School Atlas. Rev. by E. Espenshade. Rand McNally, Chicago, Ill.

Goodhart, C. B. 1958. Thrush predation on the snail *Cepaea hortensis*. J Anim. Ecol. 27:47–57.

Gottlieb, G. 1966. Species identification by avian neonates: contributory effect of perinatal auditory stimulation. Anim. Behav. 14:282–290.

Granit, R. 1955. Receptors and Sensory Perception. Yale University Press, New Haven, Conn.

Grant, P. R. 1966. Ecological compatibility of bird species on islands. Amer. Natur. 100:451–462.

Griffin, D. R. 1958. Listening in the Dark. Yale University Press, New Haven, Conn.

Grinnell, A. D. 1904. The origin and distribution of the chestnut-backed chickadee. Auk 21:364–382.

Hamilton, T. H., R. H. Booth, and I. Rubinoff. 1964. The environmental control of insular variation in bird species abundance. Proc. Nat. Acad. Sci. 52:132–140.

Hamilton, W. D. 1964. The genetical evolution of social behaviour I and II. J. Theoret. Biol. 7:1–16, 17–52.

Hardin, G. 1960. The competitive exclusion principle. Science 131:1291–1297.

Harris, V. T. 1952. An experimental study of habitat selection by prairie and forest races of the deermouse, *Peromyscus maniculatus*. Contributions to the Laboratory of Vertebrate Biology 56:1–53.

Hasler, A. D. 1956. Perception of pathways by fishes in migration. Quart. Rev. Biol. 31:200–209.

Hasler, A. D. 1960. Guideposts of migrating fishes. Science 132:785–792.

Hatch, J. 1966. Collective territories in Galapagos mockingbirds, with notes on other behavior. Wilson Bull. 78:198–207.

Hediger, H. 1942. Wildtiere in Gefangenschaft. Basel.

Hensley, M. M., and J. B. Cope. 1951. Further data on removal and repopulation of the breeding birds in a spruce-fir community. Auk 68:483–493.

Hespenheide, H. A. 1966. The selection of seed size by finches. Wilson Bull. 78:191–197.

Hilden, O. 1965. Habitat selection in birds. Annales Zoologici Fennici 2:53–75.

Hinde, R. A. 1956. The biological significance of the territories of birds. Ibis 98:340–369.

Hinde, R. A. 1966. Animal Behaviour. McGraw-Hill, N.Y.

Horner, B. E. 1954. Arboreal adaptations of *Peromyscus maniculatus* with special reference to use of the tail. Contributions to the Laboratory of Vertebrate Biology 61:1–84.

Hovanitz, W., and V. C. S. Chang. 1963. Change of food plant preference by larvae of *Pieris rapae* controlled by strain selection and the inheritance of this trait. J. Research Lepidoptera 1(2):163–168.

Howard, Eliot. 1920 (reprinted 1948). Territory in Bird Life. Collins, London.

Howells, T. H., and D. O. Vine. 1940. The innate differential in social learning. J. Abn. Soc. Psych. 35:537–548.

Hutchinson, G. E. 1959. Homage to Santa Rosalia, or Why are there so many different kinds of animals? Amer. Natur. 93:145–159.

Huxley, J. 1943. Evolution, the Modern Synthesis. Harper and Brothers, N.Y.

James, H. 1959. Flicker: an unconditioned stimulus for imprinting. Canad. J. Psych. 13:59–67.

Kear, J. 1962. Food selection in certain finches with special reference to interspecific differences. Proc. Zoolog. Soc. London 138:163–204.

Kendeigh, S. C. 1945. Community selection by birds on the Helderberg plateau of New York. Auk 62:418–436.

Kendeigh, S. C. 1961. Animal Ecology. Prentice-Hall, Englewood Cliffs, N.J.

Kettlewell, H. B. D. 1959. New aspects of the genetic control of industrial melanism in the Lepidoptera. Nature 183:918–921.

Kettlewell, H. B. D. 1965. Insect survival and selection for pattern. Science 148:1290–1296.

Kilham, P., and P. H. Klopfer. 1967. The construct "race" and the "innate differential." *In* E. Tobach *et al.* (ed.), Science and the Construct of Race. Columbia University Press, N.Y.

Kilham, P., P. H. Klopfer, and H. Oelke. 1968. Species identification and colour preferences in chicks. Anim. Behav. 16:238–244.

King, J. 1955. Social behavior, social organization and population dynamics in a black-tailed prairie dog town in the Black Hills of South Dakota. Contributions of the Laboratory of Vertebrate Biology, No. 67.

Klopfer, P. H. 1959. Social interactions in discrimination learning with special reference to feeding behaviour in birds. Behaviour 14:282–299.

Klopfer, P. H., and R. MacArthur. 1960. Niche size and faunal diversity. Amer. Natur. 87:293–300.

Klopfer, P. H., and R. H. MacArthur. 1961. On the causes of tropical species diversity, niche overlap. Amer. Natur. 95:223–226.

Klopfer, P. H. 1962. Behavioral Aspects of Ecology. Prentice-Hall, Englewood Cliffs, N.J.

Klopfer, P. H. 1963. Behavioral aspects of habitat selection: the role of early experience. Wilson Bull. 75:15–22.

Klopfer, P. H. 1964. Parameters of imprinting. Amer. Natur. 98:175–182.

Klopfer, P. H. 1965. Behavioral aspects of habitat selection. I. Wilson Bull. 77:376–381.

Klopfer, P. H., and J. P. Hailman. 1965. Habitat selection in birds. *In* D. S. Lehrman, R. A. Hinde, and E. Shaw (eds.), Advances in the

Study of Behavior, Volume I. Academic Press, N.Y. and London, p. 279–303.

Klopfer, P. H. 1965. Imprinting: a reassessment. Science 147:302–303.

Klopfer, P. H. 1967. Behavioral stereotypy in birds. Wilson Bull. 79: 290–300.

Klopfer, P. H., and J. P. Hailman. 1967. An Introduction to Animal Behavior: ethology's first century. Prentice-Hall, Englewood Cliffs. N.J.

Kropotkin, P. 1914. Mutual Aid, a Factor in Evolution. Knopf, N.Y.

Lack, D., and L. S. V. Venables. 1939. The habitat distribution of British woodland birds. J. Anim. Ecol. 8:39–71.

Lack, D. 1954. The Natural Regulation of Animal Numbers. Oxford University Press, N.Y.

Lack, D. 1966. Population Studies in Birds. Oxford University Press, N.Y.

Leach, E. 1966. Don't say "boo" to a goose. N.Y. Review of Books, Vol. VIII, No. 10.

Lehrman, D. S. 1956. On the organization of maternal behavior and the problem of instinct. *In* P. P. Grassé (ed.), L'Instinct dans le vomportement des animaux et des hommes. Masson, Paris., p. 475–520.

Lissman, H. W. 1958. On the function and evolution of electric organs in fish. J. Exper. Biol. 35:156–191.

Löhrl, H. 1959. Zur Frage des Zeitpunktes einer Prägung auf die Heimatregion beim Halsbandschnäpper (Ficedula albicollis). J. Orn. Lpz. 100:123–140.

Lorenz, K. 1965. Evolution and Modification of Behavior. University of Chicago Press, Chicago, Ill.

Lotka, A. J. 1956. Elements of Mathematical Biology. Dover Publications, N.Y.

MacArthur, R. H. 1955. Fluctuations of animal populations and a measure of community stability. Ecology 36:533–536.

MacArthur, R. H. 1958. Population ecology of some warblers of northeastern coniferous forests. Ecology 39:599–619.

MacArthur, R. H. 1959. On the breeding distribution pattern of North American migrant birds. Auk 76:318–325.

MacArthur, R. H., and J. MacArthur. 1961. On bird species diversity. Ecology 42:594–598.

MacArthur, R. H., J. W. MacArthur, and J. Preer. 1962. On bird species diversity. Amer. Natur. 96:167–174.

MacArthur, R. H., and E. O. Wilson. 1963. An equilibrium theory of insular zoogeography. Evolution 17:373–387.

MacArthur, R. H. 1964. Environmental factors affecting bird species diversity. Amer. Natur. 98:387–397.

MacArthur, R. H., and R. Levins. 1964. Competition, habitat selection and character displacement in a patchy environment. *In* Proc. Nat. Acad. Sci. 51:1207–1210.

MacArthur, R. H. 1965. Patterns of species diversity. Biolog. Revs. 40:510–533.

MacArthur, R. H., and J. H. Connell. 1966. The Biology of Population. John Wiley and Sons, N.Y.

MacArthur, R. H., H. Recher, and M. Cody. 1966. On the relation between habitat selection and species diversity. Amer. Natur., Vol. 100, 913:319–332.

Marler, P., and W. Hamilton. 1966. Mechanisms of Animal Behavior. John Wiley and Sons, N.Y.

Maturana, H. R., J. Y. Lettvin, W. S. McCulloch, and W. H. Pitts. 1960. Anatomy and physiology of vision in the frog. J. Gen. Physiol. 43:129–176.

Mayr, E. 1935. Bernard Altum and the territory theory. Proc. Linn. Soc. N.Y. 45:24–38.

Mayr, E. 1963. Animal Species and Evolution. Belknap Press, Cambridge, Mass.

Miller, A. H. 1942. Habitat selection among higher vertebrates and its relation to intraspecific variation. Amer. Natur. 76:25–35.

Miyadi, D. 1959. On some new habits and their propagation in Japanese monkey troups. XV Internat. Congr. Zool., p. 857–860.

Moreau, R. E. 1952. The place of Africa in the Palearctic migration system. J. Anim. Ecol. 21:250–271.

Newell, N. D. 1962. Paleontological gaps and geochronology. J. Paleont. 36:592–610.

Nice, M. M. 1941. The role of territory in bird life. Amer. Midl. Natur. 26:441–487.

Noble, G. K. 1939. The role of dominance on the social life of birds. Auk 56:263–273.

Odum, E. 1959. Fundamentals of Ecology. W. B. Saunders, Philadelphia.

Orians, G. 1961. The ecology of blackbird social systems. Ecolog. Monogr. 31:285–312.

Palmgren, P. 1938. Zur Kausalanalyse der ökologischen und Geographischen Verbreitung der Vögel Nordeuropas. Arch. f. Naturgenchichte 7:235–269.

Palmgren, P. 1943. Zur Biologie von Regulus r. regulus (1.) und Parus atricapillus borealis Selys. Eine vergleichende und ökologische Untersuchung. Acta Zool. Fennica 14:1–113.

Palmgren, P. 1949. Welche Faktoren bedingen die geographische und topographische Verbreitung der Vogel? Folia Biotheor. 4:23–40.

Park, T. 1962. Beetles, competition, and populations. Science 138:1369–1374.

Pfaffmann, C. 1955. Gustatory nerve impulses in rat, cat and rabbit. J. Neurophysiol. 18:429–440.

Pitelka, F. A. 1941. Distribution of birds in relation to major biotic communities. Amer. Midl. Natur. 25:113–137.

Preston, F. W. 1948. The commonness and rarity of species. Ecology 29:254–283.

Ricklefs, R. E. 1966. The temporal component of diversity among species of birds. Evolution 20:235–242.

Riopelle, A. J. 1960. Observational learning of a position habit by monkeys. J. Comp. Physiol. Psychol. 53:426–428.

Sabine, W. S. 1955. The winter society of the Oregon junco: the flock. Condor 57:88–111.

Schaller, G. B. 1963. The Mountain Gorilla. University of Chicago Press, Chicago, Ill.

Schmidt-Koenig, K. 1965. Current problems in bird orientation. In D. S. Lehrman, R. A. Hinde, and E. Shaw (eds.), Advances in the Study of Behavior. Vol. I. Academic Press, N.Y. and London. p. 217–278.

Schmidt-Nielsen, K., and Y. T. Kim. 1964. The effect of salt intake on the size and function of the salt gland of ducks. Auk 81:160–172.

Sexton, O. J., H. Heatwole, and D. Knight. 1964. Correlation of microdistribution of some Panamanian reptiles and amphibians with structural organization of the habitat. Carib. J. Sci. 4(1): 261–295.

Shelford, V. E. 1913. Animal Communities in Temperate America. University of Chicago Press, Chicago, Ill.

Siegel, H. S., and P. B. Siegel. 1961. The relationship of social competition with endocrine weights and activity in male chickens. Anim. Behav. 9:151–158.

Skinner, B. F. 1966. The phylogeny and ontogeny of behavior. Science 153:1205–1213.

Slobodkin, B. L. 1961. Growth and Regulation in Animal Populations. Holt, Rinehart and Winston, N.Y.

Sluckin, W. 1965. Imprinting and Early Learning. Aldine, Chicago, Ill., and Methuen and Co., London.

Spencer, H. 1896. First Principles. D. Appleton, N.Y.

Stebbins, G. L., Jr. 1950. Variation and Evolution in Plants. Columbia University Press, N.Y.

Stenger, J. 1958. Food habits and available food of ovenbirds in relation to territory size. Auk 75:335–346.

Sumner, F. B. 1935a. Studies of protective color change. Proc. Nat. Acad. Sci. 21:345–353.

Sumner, F. B. 1935b. Evidence for protective value of changeable color in fish. Amer. Natur. 69:245–266.

Sunkel, W. 1928. Bedeutung optischer Eindrücke der Vögel fur die Wahl ihres Aufenthaltortes. Zeitschrift fur wissensch. Zool. 132:171–175.

Sutherland, N. S. 1960. Theories of shape discrimination in octopus. Nature. London. 186:1092–1094.

Svärdson, G. 1949. Competition and habitat selection in birds. Oikos 1:157–174.

Takata, N. 1961. Studies on the host preference of common cabbage butterfly, *Pieris rapae crucivora* (Boisduval): XII Successive rearing of the cabbage butterfly larva with certain host plants and its effect on the oviposition preference of the adult. Japan J. Ecol. 2:147–154.

Tansley, A. G. 1935. The rise and abuse of vegetational concepts and terms. Ecology 16:284–307.

Thorpe, W. H. 1956. Learning and Instinct in Animals. Methuen, London.

· Tinbergen, N. 1953. The Herring Gull's World. Collins, London.

Turner, E. R. A. 1961. Survival values of different methods of camouflage as shown in a model population. Proc. Zoolog. Soc. London 136: 273–284.

Turner, E. R. A. 1964. Social feeding in birds. Behaviour 24:1–46.

Vernadsky, W. I. 1945. The biosphere and the noosphere. Amer. Sci. 33:1–12.

Von Frisch, K. 1965. Tanzsprache und Orientierung der Biene. Springer, Berlin.

von Uexküll, J. 1921. Umwelt und Innenwelt der Tiere. Springer, Berlin.

Waddington, C. 1960. The Ethical Animal. George Allen and Unwin, London.

Wallgren, V. H. 1954. Energy metabolism of two species of the genus Emberiza as correlated with distribution and migration. Acta Zoologica Fennica 84:1–110.

Wasilewski, A. 1961. Certain aspects of the habitat selection of birds. Ekologia Polska. Seria A. Warszawa. 9:111–137.

Watson, A. 1967. Population control by territorial behavior in red grouse. Nature 215:1274–1275.

Wecker, S. C. 1963. The role of early experience in habitat selection by the prairie deer mouse, *Peromyscus maniculatus bairdi.* Ecolog. Monogr. 33:307–325.

Wells, M. J. 1962. Brain and Behaviour in Cephalopods. Stanford University Press, Stanford, Calif.

Whittaker, R. H. 1956. Vegetation of the Great Smoky Mountains. Ecolog. Monogr. 26:1–80.

Wiens, J .A. 1966. On group selection and Wynne-Edwards' hypothesis. Amer. Scient. 54:273–287.

Williams, G. C. 1966. Adaptation and Natural Selection. Princeton University Press, Princeton, N.J.

Wolfson, A. 1959. The role of light and darkness in the regulation of spring migration and reproductive cycles in birds. Photoperiodism and Related Phenomena in Plants and Animals, 679–716.

Wynne-Edwards, V. C. 1962. Animal Dispersion in Relation to Social Behaviour. Hafner, N.Y.

Young, J. Z. 1961. Learning and discrimination in the octopus. Biolog. Revs. 36:32–96.

INDEX